Gorgeous
Elena

The
Sacred
Quest

You are a beautiful
Star & your essence is
so magnificent that I am
stunned .... you are soooo
beautiful
much love ♡ & hugs
Angelica xxx

The Sacred Quest

by
Louise E. Langley

ETHER
PUBLISHING

First edition published 2007
by Ether Publishing
www.thesacredquest.co.uk

ISBN 978-1-906437-00-8

A CIP catalogue record for this book is available
from the British Library.

Every care has been taken that all information was
correct at the time of going to press. The publishers
accept no responsibility for any error in detail,
inaccuracy or judgement whatsoever.

Publishing Project Management
by Pencil-Sharp Ltd

Designed and typeset
by Pencil-Sharp Ltd

Printed and bound in Great Britain
by Clays, Suffolk

FSC

Mixed Sources
Product group from well-managed
forests and other controlled sources

Cert no. SGS - COC - 2061
www.fsc.org
© 1996 Forest Stewardship Council

In service to truth
And love
And for Ben

Contents

This book does not conform to traditional
literary etiquette.

It is simply a message of truth
and inspiration.

Please read it from your heart.

In this way you will facilitate your own
Sacred Quest.

Prologue

This story, whilst presented within this book as a novel, is in fact an account of the extraordinary events that have happened in my life over the past eighteen months.

… my journey began some six months beforehand, the moment I purchased and bestowed upon myself a particular ring from Edinburgh Castle.

This ring is inscribed with an ogham script taken directly from a whorl stone excavated on the island of Orkney. The translation of the script reads 'A blessing on the soul of L' and this it has truly been!

Many of the people I have encountered throughout my journey have chosen to be presented in this book using their true identity. This of course includes myself. For those who do not wish to be called by their real names, or those I have not been able to ask, I have given them different names. The hardest name of all for me to change is that of my sacred partner who, as I finally finish writing, has not yet physically met me. His name carries such purity of energy that my only hope is that the name I have given him carries that extraordinary energy throughout the pages of this book.

It is to him that I dedicate this book.

* * *

Certain terminology used as the story unfolds is explained towards the back of this book. This includes a brief description of Ascended Masters, the Angelic Realm, Crystals and chakras, and many of the scientific evolutionary terms I refer to. I feel it is important, before you begin to read, that you understand the importance these areas have played in my unfolding journey, and that by noting these incredible signs around me as they have appeared, I have enabled this journey to unfold in the manner in which it has. Often the subtlest of signs has been the signpost to the direction I had to take. We need only open our eyes and acknowledge these signs for every person to discover their true journey!

When I speak of my 'knowing', I refer to that feeling deep within which presents itself to me as an understanding, an intuition, a gut feeling. This feeling from the inner self is in fact, quite literally, the soul's direction, the soul's message. Only when you begin to follow your knowing implicitly, will miracles begin to unfold around you in an astonishing manner. This inspiration, this miraculous journey, is every person's birthright, not simply that of the gifted master. As your journey unfolds, so you begin to understand that life is love and love is life. When you live your life in love and trust, all will come to pass as you believe it should, as you intend it to. This is true of relationships, the healing of our illnesses, the healing of our cities, and the restoration to harmony and balance of our planet.

I hear you consider, 'How could I possibly find my love of the ages, a love so extraordinary upon this planet when its population totals over six billion people? It would be like looking for a needle in a haystack?' I would simply reply by telling you this. When you place all of your trust upon your soul's direction, upon this inner feeling, when you follow at all times your intuition, without delay, without question and in absolute determination to delight upon its instruction, then you need look for nothing. This love, together with its miraculous journey, will quite literally come and find you! As will the most incredible sense of inner peace, which utterly fills your entire being, inspire those around you as they watch you radiate with an energy they wish to reach out and touch, to emulate. For there is no greater teacher than your inspiration, than the energy of the love of life.

This inner knowing has been, and remains always, the predominant factor in the unfolding of my journey.

I mention 'Pioneers' within the story. These are those people, those visionaries, who are to drive forward the radical changes I am directed to instigate upon the planet. These changes were outlined in totality, impregnated into my consciousness during the space of one night, as I awoke with a knowing of an amazing story unfolding within my mind. As I wrote through the night I was staggered as I took in the enormity of what I had just committed to paper, much of which I had neither heard of, nor understood. I have been guided that this book lays down a gauntlet to those pioneers who have not yet stepped forward. These changes are, of course, but a part of the entire story.

Numbers have, and continue to play a huge role in the messages sent to me. This began when, so early in this journey, I started to notice sequences of numbers in threes being presented to me in many different forms simultaneously. For example, three cars would pass with number plates registering 999, 888, 444. It would seem always to be as I was considering something for which I wanted an answer, a direction. I was guided to a book written by Doreen Virtue called *Angel Numbers*, which explains that numbers presented in threes are a clear, universal indication of a message being emphasised in answer to a question, or a thought. From then on I found myself decoding longer sequences of numbers and letters, as if decoding a cryptic code, which always seemed to be presented in perfect timing, and answered in totality, a thought or a question I was pondering.

In truth, and to the amazement of those around me, so many signs were given in so many different forms to continually support me, direct me, and to substantiate the actions I was taking as a direct result of following my intuition. So many people, places and events were given to me to provide the tools and ability to walk this journey, and to arrive at the place I find myself now, in this moment of now.

'This moment of now' is a term you will encounter many times within this book. This is one of the most powerful concepts to embrace and emulate, for once you understand that all is created *in* this moment of now, *from* this moment of now, you understand the power you hold at your fingertips to utterly bask in the bliss of life. Everything within the universe, across all of creation's cycles, is in this moment of now. There is no time. To be the master of your life, you must understand that all that you do in this moment of now affects and creates all that you are to be, all that you have been, and all that you are across all of creation's cycles. You always become what you believe yourself to be right now, in this moment of now.

I find myself now, an ordinary young woman upon an extraordinary journey, who is utterly blessed beyond measure. I see this life through the eyes of a child, for I know now that this is how life is to be experienced. The innocence and delight in the magic and mystique of the utter trust we should always place upon our soul, upon our intuition, is the greatest gift we could ever have bestowed upon ourselves. Life is abundant, it is beauty and we need only to trust in this to watch the miracle of life we intended for ourselves to unfold.

Finally I would like to introduce the term, 'Oneness', which through the pages of this book, I intend for all to come to fully understand. As I have quite incredibly found myself refuting and sometimes concurring with scientific reports, to draw together the different elements explored in fringe science, with my understanding of the oneness of the universal energy, that which I am given and directed to expand, I find that the most important message for the world to embrace is that of oneness. This literally means that we always have been, and always will be, different, beautiful and divine expressions of the very same energy source, the one.

Science has proven this now. You need only consider the area of quantum physics and its knowing of the one energy source, of the behaviour of photons of light, of atoms within that one energy source which quite clearly show the ability to track more than one path simultaneously, to quite literally live in parallel dimensions. Science is fast embracing the knowing, the basis and the truth of the term many would give 'spirituality', and yet it is my belief that this term must now be replaced by the term, 'Oneness'. For it is certain that, with the clear teachings that can now be instigated so that this term is understood, so will begin the path to love and trust for all, to the abundance of life, to sacred union. So will the Sacred Quest be complete.

The Sacred Quest

Chapter 1

Tossing clothes into her suitcase in her usual, haphazard manner, Louise paused momentarily to clasp back her long dark hair and ponder what lay in her future. As she considered the weekend ahead in Dublin with friends, her thoughts drifted once more to the conundrum she found herself with. How was she to dissolve her marriage, a marriage in which she had been deeply unhappy for some years now? Ever since she was a child she had experienced feelings of incredible love within lives long past, as if a memory of having lived and loved many times before. She had no idea, in that moment, that this weekend was about to unearth the reality of these feelings in the most spectacular way.

Louise was an attractive woman, with a kind of Celtic beauty, an artistic, quirky style and a fun-loving, compassionate nature. She truly loved life. A mother of three, she had had a successful career in the world of finance, and had recently set up her own design business. She was looking forward to this well-deserved trip to Dublin with her friends.

Her husband of twelve years was fundamentally a good man, kind-hearted but diametrically opposed in every way to her beliefs and character. She had been finding their life together increasingly difficult for some years now, and had been struggling deeply with the ethical and moral dilemma she found herself in. Should she stay in a marriage in which she found herself filling her time purely to distract herself from the core of her unhappiness? For she had been unhappy for many years now. This was the kind of unhappiness that occurs when a person is not true to themself, when they live their life to serve others, never to honour their own truth.

Her concern was also for her children. How could she separate from her husband and create a situation where they would live their young lives being shared between two households, potentially rocking their stability and sense of security? On the other hand, how fair was it to bring them up in the environment of a loveless marriage where their role model for relationships was one of a husband and wife who felt no real warmth or mutual admiration for one another?

She knew her husband would never leave her, and would rather choose to live a life of mediocrity with her in order to provide a strong base for their children. She admired his strength of character and the reasoning behind his decisions, but knew that the basis of their relationship was not a healthy one, either for her or for the future of her children. She had been quite ill over the past couple of years and knew that this had been caused by her avoidance of the inevitable decision she knew she had to make. She also knew that if she didn't make a decision now, her illness would get far worse. She was an avid believer in alternative medicine and knew that almost all bodily ailments were a direct result of underlying emotional causes, and that the only way to remove these bodily ailments was to remove those latent causes. What good could she possibly be as a mother to her children if she were ill, frustrated, depressed and had lost all love of life? The very qualities she needed to be able to share with her children for their growth, were the ones that were slowly dying as each day went past. She saw the effect her unhappiness was having upon them and it made her heart break. They deserved so much more than this. She deserved much more than this. She knew that she could return to her true self if she were prepared to have the courage to walk her path in life, to be true to her soul. Only then could she look after them in the way they deserved.

This decision had weighed heavily upon her for so long now, that it was with great relief that she was to be going to Dublin for a few days with some friends to celebrate a birthday. It would provide her with the opportunity to forget for a short while that which she knew she could put off no longer.

From the moment they arrived, their days were filled with laughter and fun, shopping and the kind of chatter that means something only to close friends, those who have experienced so much together, exchanging knowing glances, reading each others minds and thoughts. They all experienced so much that weekend, with no need for questions or explanations. They were all simply comfortable in each other's company, slipping easily into each other's space and moments.

They had decided to celebrate their last night in style, choosing to start the evening at a Taste of Dublin event held in Dublin Castle. As they stood on its balcony in the early evening mist, overlooking the stunning grounds and sipping cocktails that had been perfected by the duty barmen, Louise slipped once again into a distant memory of a life gone past. So many times in her life had she experienced complete knowing of times and places which had existed many lifetimes ago, as if the reality of the past were present in that moment. She knew within her soul that her connection to Ireland was a powerful one. She and this land had made pacts, which, somehow, she had to fulfil.

Throughout her life she had been drawn to everything with a Celtic link: music, arts and of course, the people themselves; beautiful, wonderful joyous people; lovers of life who were deeply impassioned in their views. For several years so many paths in her life had drawn her back to Ireland, and here she was again, taking in the air that seemed to her to be the very breath of life itself. How deeply she resonated with the energies of this beautiful land and its people.

Mesmerised by the moment, she suddenly realised that she ought to check that the children were okay, and chose that moment to phone home. It was as if she already had a sense of what was coming because, as her husband spoke, her soul sang its final knowing within her. It filled Louise with an overwhelming knowing that the end had now come. Finally she understood that from that very moment, she must be true to herself, and with that came the understanding that upon her return to England, she must commit to what she had been unable to bring herself to do for these many years. Somehow she must find a way to lovingly and compassionately dissolve this marriage while ensuring that their children continued to feel secure, loved and cherished. But how?

Infused with the sweet feelings induced by the alcohol, her emotions ran high. She looked around at her friends, listening to their slightly drunken laughter, and went through the motions as the young male singing quartet began to serenade them. As one grabbed hold of her hand to dance with her, and then got down on one knee to sing to her, it was as if everything within this reality became surreal. She drank more and more, trying to numb the feelings running deep within her soul, until finally she could do it no longer. She collapsed in a dark and quiet corner, threw her head into her hands, and for the first time within this lifetime prayed with all the strength and force of her soul to the universe. She pleaded with the universe to send her the guidance and clarity she knew she needed. Sobbing and overwrought with intense physical emotion, she begged for the kind of guidance that would leave her in no doubt as to the path that would serve her highest good from this moment on.

As she began to pull herself together, thoughts of a man started to drift into her mind, gently tugging at her consciousness. So many times had she seen this man in her dream state, and his image had always inspired in her an incredible feeling of returning home. She sought out her friends and together they left the Castle to move on to another bar, the thoughts of the man still fleeting in and out of her mind.

* * *

Later that evening they decided to go to a late-night bar near the hotel where they were staying. It was just what Louise needed. Her spirits had begun to lift as she began to see that her future lay in her own hands. In the bar, men were hitting on them continually, buying drinks, dancing, and begging her to settle in the West Country with them. They made her laugh so much, their wit and charm so typical of the famous Irish blarney. As one guy, on bended knee, was holding her hand and making her cry with laughter in a way that was reminiscent of so many evenings she had spent in Ireland in the past, she felt the door of the bar open behind her. Before she even turned to face him, she felt the full force of his energy enter that place. She knew as she turned to look upon his face that her life was about to change forever, for in that moment, as their eyes met, an incredible bolt of energy, a connection the like of which she had never experienced in this life, occurred.

His friend turned back to the door to leave and he followed, turning back to her, imploring her with his eyes to follow him. This man took her breath away, for he was the very man she had seen so many times in her dreams. He was tall, slim, with long dark hair that fell across his face, a slightly shaded beard, feline features and the most beautiful, piercing dark eyes. She stood in that bar as he walked out onto the street, feeling as if a part of her very soul had left her. After a few moments, when she could resist the screams of her soul no longer, she did something that she had never done before in her life. She followed, implicitly, utterly and without question, her intuition. Her intuition told her to go out and look for him. And she did.

As she stepped outside and looked up he was there, standing as if waiting for her and expecting her to come out. He smiled at her and they started to talk. As they stood out on the street in the cold night, talking at length, it was as if all else faded from reality. All attachments, all obligations faded from their vision as they basked in the beauty of those moments. He looked deep into her eyes, piercing her very soul with his knowing, and it was as if time stood still. It felt so familiar for her to be with him, she felt deeply moved to be standing in the presence of his energy. When she explained this to him he gently stroked her hair and held her arms, saying that he would never forget her. He pulled her face up to his, looked deep into her eyes once more, telling her how beautiful she was. There was so much love between them, lifetimes upon lifetimes of love exploding in one eternal moment. It seemed as if a shining light enveloped them, casting all else into shadow. As he leant towards her, holding her hair, and gently kissed her, she understood in that moment that this man was not new to her experience. She began to remember an incredible and overwhelming feeling of pure, spiritual, joyous love as their souls connected.

At that moment her friends reappeared, merry with alcohol and desperate to move on. As she started to introduce him to them, they grabbed her arm, insisting they leave immediately, telling her that they were saving her from herself. They literally took her by the arm and steered her away. Incredulously, she allowed them to do so, swept up in the intensity of the moment. As, momentarily, she turned back towards him she felt her heart crumble to see him with tears upon his face. Her friends raced her on and out of his sight and, as she wept, trying to explain through her tears that they didn't know what they had done, she realised that she had no way of contacting this man. All she knew about him was that his name was Adrian, and that he lived some way outside of Dublin.

Back in her hotel room she lay down on her bed, but could not sleep. She really had no desire for life, for it felt as if her life had been wrenched away, so deep ran the vibration of that love and the tragedy of its loss in entirety. She flew home to London the next evening in a trance, lost for words and with no desire to be in contact with the world we feel and hear.

Chapter 2

The week stretched ahead of her as if it were an eternity. So many times had she pondered, deliberated and struggled with inner knowing that what was within her must be drawn forth. Now, that knowing was accompanied by an overwhelming feeling of lost love. She had, since a tiny girl, always known that a love of such purity, such intensity could exist between two people whose souls were connected in this way. Throughout her life she had experienced flashbacks to former existences, as if they were dreams, or visions, and yet they were accompanied by such profound feelings not possible unless they had been experienced truly as reality. She knew this was no dream. She knew as surely as she could feel the rough wooden floor beneath her feet, as surely as she could hear the bird song in the trees outside, as surely as she could feel the intensity of the sun streaming through the window and warming her face, that she had loved this man many times. Why then had the universe brought him to her and so swiftly taken him away? What was the purpose of this? She could see only darkness, a kind of darkness that prevails when dark nights fill your very existence, when the body is struggling for truth and direction, not realising that the soul is now to begin that search.

As the week passed, never before had she craved solitude so, for it was that she needed to grieve, to commune with herself, to understand now, finally, who and what she was, and how this related to all of the experiences she had had, and to her understanding of the universe and her place within it. She withdrew completely from everyone and everything, much to the dismay of all those around her. People were so used to her presence, her vibrant energy, her love of life, and they were deeply concerned with what they perceived to be occurring in front of their eyes. To the world at large she was quite literally falling apart.

Although the knowing of all that lay ahead should have overwhelmed her, she could only focus upon the grief within. She came to realise that this grief was for herself, for although she had found and then lost the love of this man, the realisation was creeping upon her that this was really grief brought about by not living her truth, of being somebody she was not for so long now. She had been so driven to live the life of the person that society expected of her that she had, in the process, completely abandoned the call from within her, the call to live and walk the truth of who she was. And who was that person? If she knew only one thing, it was that the quest to find herself must now commence. She could now only live in a state of love. After all, surely life was love and love was life itself. What other purpose was there for living if not to exist in love?

* * *

As she got up very early the weekend following her return, she crept downstairs, careful not to wake anyone, and sat quietly in a room facing the garden so that she could watch the dawn mist rise across the distant fields beyond the glass doors. As she sat, she started to feel a sense of incredible calm descend upon her, cutting through the heaviness of her heart. She felt as if her soul were rising within her, elevating itself from somewhere above her stomach, through her body and up and out of the crown of her head, until she felt as if her consciousness was somewhere above her body. As she sat in this meditative state, she pleaded for understanding. Without comprehending what she was doing, she sent waves of thought to the universe in a request to be given an understanding of what was happening to her right now.

As she focused intently upon receiving an answer, she felt the calm expand throughout her consciousness. After a few minutes she somehow brought herself back to the awareness of sitting in the room, and opened her eyes wide. At that moment two beautiful white doves flew into the garden and stopped at the foot of the doors in front of her. One nuzzled the other's neck, and as both looked intently at Louise, the most incredible feeling of universal joy and love filled her senses. After a minute or so, they flew away, leaving her contemplating how, in twelve years of living at her house, she had never once seen even a single white dove anywhere within her garden, and that this was in some way a response to her plea for understanding. She did not realise that this was to precipitate an avalanche of communication between herself and the universe from now on: the beginning of her journey to understanding.

* * *

The week that followed brought revelations. On a constant roller coaster of emotions Louise was bewildered as she found trails of white feathers laid out around her house each day. The children denied having put them there and she, weak now from not eating or sleeping properly, was not about to challenge them. In fact, she believed that they were coming from a different source altogether, for she was now starting to feel the presence of spiritual beings with her, protecting her and emanating love. She felt whispers of touch against her skin, her cheek, holding her hand. While she had always believed that guardian angels existed to guide you through your life, she certainly had never felt the presence of such beings before. She was not at all frightened, only confused, and realised that she needed help to understand what was happening. She bought a magazine she had seen advertised at a Mind Body and Spirit exhibition the year before and asked to be guided to someone who could help her. As the pages fell open her gaze was drawn to a particular clairvoyant's advertisement. She had never contacted a clairvoyant before, even though so many times she had been drawn to explore the flashbacks of past lives she had experienced. Certainly she had been considering past life regression for some time now, always a little wary of what it might uncover.

She called Liya, the clairvoyant named in the advertisement, and proceeded to have her first reading. This
reading was quite astonishing in its accuracy. Without
any prompting, or knowledge being revealed by Louise at all, Liya proceeded to tell Louise all that had been
happening to her over the past few years. She described
her dilemma, her children, how she had taken a trip
across the water, leaving with a heavy heart, knowing
that decisions loomed regarding her marriage. She then
proceeded to describe in great detail the bar in which
she had met Adrian, describing the panelled wall, the
narrow stretch with a dip halfway that was where she
had tripped with her friend. She described Adrian's
physical appearance in astonishingly accurate detail,
and the deep connection that had happened between
them. She explained that he had been sent to Louise
to show her the beautiful, joyous and spiritual union
they had shared during many lifetimes together, and
to reflect the love in Louise that was her soul. It was as
if he had held up a mirror for her to see that she was
this beauty, this love that she had abandoned. He was a
beacon in the darkness, the beginning of her journey to
the discovery of her soul, her self. Only the power of a
soulmate, of a love so strong, could have brought about
the final catalyst to propel her on her journey. Now
was the time for her soul to speak, for her to be in this
incarnation who she had intended, to do what she had
intended. She must be strong now and trust her soul's
guidance, to follow implicitly, as she already had, her
soul's messages.

Now more withdrawn, unable to sleep and grieving for the loss of this man as though she had just lost the love of her life, Louise pleaded for guidance to help her get through the here and now. She implored the universe to send her the kind of guidance that would help her to sort through the process of trying to separate now from her husband without hurting him or the children. She could not see how this would be possible and yet knew now that it was essential that it happen. She knew her husband would find it impossible to understand that she still cared for him, but did not love him as a wife should love a husband. She opened the magazine once more and was guided to call Angel, a lady who offered assistance by healing through the angelic realm.

The emotions within Louise overflowed as she spoke. Her voice was barely audible through the tears that were flowing freely. Angel quietly and calmly explained that she knew exactly what Louise was going through. 'I know what you feel. For many it is hard to comprehend where you are, but I understand what it is like to experience the love of a soulmate in a meeting such as you had. The intensity of that love spans lifetimes, eons of incarnations and therefore it stands to reason that the effect is astounding, especially when you both understand the connection runs so deep. But your path now is for you. To be absolutely sure that this is your chosen path you must now concentrate upon why your soul has brought you to this place, and why you have decided to end your marriage. You have been gifted with a beautiful awakening and, although it hurts right now, you will in time understand why meeting your soulmate and then being immediately separated was the right path for you. For it is not about the love he had for you, but about recognising the love that is within you, that is you. You are love and light. This is your soul. You already know that and when he looked into your eyes, he saw the beauty and radiant glow of your soul. The love you saw reflected in his eyes was, quite literally, you.'

Louise did know this. She also knew that the universe had brought this man to her, after already deciding to end the marriage, in order to ensure that she understood that her dreams were not in fact dreams at all, but recall of what was, and what should always be, perfect love. 'As you go away over the summer and sit by the water's edge, the power of the sea will start to heal you, to clear your thoughts, bring your soul's complete knowing to you, and by the time the summer is through you will be ready to embrace your future. This period of awakening can only start when you have cleared your soul of what is no longer needed, only then can you start to rebuild. The angelic realm are with you now, protecting you and guiding you. This is the presence you feel around you constantly. The trails of feathers are messages left by them to indicate to you their presence and support. The universe is holding you. Allow the universe to communicate with you through the clear channels which have already opened for you and which are opening more, moment by moment. Notice and trust implicitly all of the signs you are given. They are in everything.'

Angel told Louise to take away with her a book by Gary Zukav named *Seat of the Soul*. She explained that reading this book would enable Louise to bring forth answers from within, and that answers from within are the greatest knowledge. 'Understand and respect the fact that your husband is on his path too. You both, at soul level, agreed to play a part in each other's lives here before you were incarnated this time. To understand within yourself what that role is, and to completely fulfil that role, to bring it to completion, is exactly what you should aspire to. Always understand that the soul does everything from love, because the soul is only love. Your children chose you two as parents, knowing the path that lay ahead, knowing that this was part of what they chose to experience in this lifetime. If you walk your path in love and light then the footprints you leave are those of light. Continue to follow your soul's messages in absolute obedience and you will only ever leave a trail of light for all to follow.'

* * *

The following morning, as Louise rose, she looked through the bedroom window out at the clear blue sky and marvelled at how two extremely long streams of cloud seemed to form an almost perfect cross that spanned her entire vision. As she opened the conservatory doors out to the garden she was preoccupied with the thought that when you know in your heart that you want something so much, this must be part of your soul's plan on earth, and all of the universe will conspire to help you achieve it. As she glanced down, her mouth fell open in astonishment. Here at her feet lay the beginning of a trail of about three hundred white feathers, which wound down across the grass, through the trees, and came to rest in a circle around her favourite tree at the foot of her garden. As she sat down cross-legged under this tree, basking in the early morning sun, she looked up to see that the cross of clouds was even more defined than it had been minutes before, with not another cloud visible in the sky, and she knew somehow that this was a message for her.

Sitting in her bed that night, on the eve of her and the children's departure to Crete, she asked the universe to please give her some sign of exactly who and what she was. As she declared her request, the most incredible white light blazed across the sky in front of her eyes. She stood, walked to the window and opened it. It must have been a streak of lightning, she rationalised, feeling the cool air brush against her cheek. No sooner had she thought this than the entire sky lit white in front of her once more, staying that way for a few moments. This was not the white light of lightning; she felt within her heart the knowing that this was indeed the essence of life, for this white light radiated with magnificence as it lit the entire sky. As she lay in wonder back in her bed, she felt the undeniable presence of the universe around her, and for the first time since her return from Dublin, knew that she would never be alone at any point again.

Chapter 3

As she stepped onto the beach in Crete the following evening, Louise felt the late evening sun gently caress her skin, the sea wash around her feet, and as she dived under the water she knew that this time ahead was for healing now. She sat on the wooden jetty, looking out to sea, and beyond to the island of Spinalonga, shadowed in the dipping sun. Watching the waves rolling in towards her, the children playing on the beach below, her hair blowing gently behind her in the breeze, she chatted idly to a Greek waiter, one of her many friends in Crete. Yes, this next month would be Louise's restoration, her clearing and her definition of her future.

Everywhere she went that summer, every friend who saw her remarked upon the glow emanating from her. She passed many evenings and lazy afternoons in her favourite café bar, The Pine Tree Kafenion, which was run and owned by her dear friend Stephanie. Holidaymakers, friends and locals met here, laughing and chatting while children drifted in and out from the beach and the village of Plaka. All the guys she knew remarked upon her radiance and the sense of peace about her. Many evenings were passed in the company of these friends, listening to the dulcet tones of the ethnic music she loved, sipping long, cool margaritas, and enjoying deep discussions. Her fluency in the Greek language, learnt as the children had grown, meant that she was now able to have long, meaningful discussions, and enjoy laughter with the locals.

Every day that passed brought messages to her from the universe. It seemed that nature was constantly sending her reassurance. She found petals in the garden laid out in the shape of hearts, flocks of birds singing in the dark of night, and large snowy owls, frequently waiting upon her gate, as if they were a welcoming committee. Although the house was at the foot of the mountains, it was unusual to have a large snowy owl greeting you every evening.

As the Cretan sun rose early one morning, Louise set off for Spinalonga Island with her dear childhood friend and now sister-in-law Gillian, who had come with her children to stay for a week. As they strolled under the increasingly suffocating heat, the familiar emotions she always felt here began to well up within her. This island had been used not only as a Turkish prisoner-of-war camp, but also most heart-wrenchingly as a leper colony. As she stood within the colony's old cleansing chamber, tiny barred windows that faced straight out to sea allowing the only natural light to enter, she was suddenly rooted to the spot, surrounded by what seemed to be an enormous shaft of tubular light rising from the floor beneath her and passing through the ceiling above. As this tubular shaft of light grew in intensity, she closed her eyes and felt the presence of many beings. She wasn't sure what they were trying to communicate to her but felt their presence urging her to understand. As she left the chamber and walked, trance-like, around the rest of the island, she felt as if an inner knowing was being brought forth. It was as if some distant memory was being gently loosened from her subconscious.

* * *

One day later in the holiday, when Louise was feeling particularly low, contemplating the prospect that she would never see Adrian again in this lifetime, and wondering what the future would hold, she arranged to meet friends at a hotel they were staying at. As she and a friend swam out to sea, leaving the kids playing on the beach, she felt the knowing of somebody watching her. She glanced back to the beach, and there, standing on the shoreline, was a man that looked so like Adrian she had to double take. He dived into the sea and swam out to where they were swimming. He looked at her, smiled and swam away, glancing back as he did so. After a few minutes he swam back past them again and smiled intently. Louise smiled back and continued chatting with her friend. As they swam back into shore she noticed him lying on a sunbed next to a girl, his partner she presumed. He looked up at her as she passed smiling again, and when she heard him talking she realised that he was Irish. Why was he smiling at her when he was clearly with somebody else? She couldn't resist noticing every time he looked at her and as she was packing up to leave, she noticed him walk past with his partner as if heading back to his hotel room. He hesitated and, as the girl with him stopped to talk to somebody, he turned and looked intently at Louise. He was deliberating, she knew this much, for she knew herself what it felt like not to follow the instincts within. But she was not about to come between a man and his partner. He smiled at her and she turned away. On this day, the universe had sent her a reminder of Adrian, but also a message that love was to be pure, and that each person must choose their own path. She was not ready for anything but the clearing of her soul, the discovery of her path and the task of dissolving her marriage in the most loving manner possible. These were the tasks she knew lay ahead of her now.

When her husband arrived towards the end of her stay in Crete, it was the hardest time she had ever spent in his company, for she knew this to be the time to explain properly that she must draw this marriage to its close. She had wanted to wait until they were returning home so that he and the children would be relaxed for their time here, but pressed by him for an explanation of all that was happening, she spent many days explaining why their marriage would now have to end. This was a time that required great strength. It would have been so easy to relent, to choose the path of least resistance once more, but she knew that in doing so it was a disservice to him, to the children and to herself. She had begun to find an incredible inner peace, find the love that was her. She knew there was no going back and so she continued to try to lovingly explain why the time to begin the process of their separation must be now.

* * *

One magical evening passed as she sat with Stephanie, looking out to sea in the dark hours around midnight, only candles and the shadow of the moon streaked across the sea to illuminate the dark of night. They talked conspiratorially about their knowing of universal law, of the mystique and magic of life, of creation and of the wonders unfolding around them, and as they spoke, the most incredible set of events began to unfold. Each of the candles suddenly blew out, the moon grew in size and seemingly smiled upon them. Louise watched the moon mouth a message to her. She could not understand what it was she wanted to tell her, but she knew that it was important that some day she would understand. From nowhere a mist drew in across the sea and the night became completely silent. Nobody could be seen or heard – a situation that was incomprehensible for that time of night in that village. Louise and Stephanie looked at one other as both realised that they were surrounded by the presence of the most incredible energy. They felt it surround and protect them, and felt it within them.

As Stephanie talked of Georgos, one of the men in the bar they both really liked, and the way that he was so in touch with himself, a feature which was atypical of Greek men, and how, although he lived just a few doors along from Stephanie, he never came to see her upon his return in all the time he had worked for her, he appeared on his bike through the mist as if from nowhere. It was almost pitch black where they were sitting now, almost impossible now for the naked eye to distinguish anything, the only light being cast from the moon. Georgos dismounted from his bike and for the first time ever, walked straight into Stephanie's garden to where the two girls were sitting in the absolute silence of the night. It was as if he had been drawn by an invisible thread of energy. As Stephanie sat, in absolute amazement, he walked straight up to Louise, kissed her on the cheek, told her she was beautiful, chatted for a moment with them both and then went to his room. As Stephanie sat, mouth agape at the timing and the event, the power which had been lost around the whole village hours before quite suddenly came back on. Louise kissed her friend goodnight and made her way back to the villa. As she passed Georgos's bike she smiled as she noticed that the mileage on the dash in the car read 4444. Any number presented in three (or more) of the same digit represented the universe's confirmation of a message, and Louise, having read a book by Doreen Virtue about universal messages, understood that this number was confirmation that she was surrounded by thousands of angels right now!

Chapter 4

L ouise was back home in England for only a week before setting off to Italy to stay with friends in the Tuscan mountains. She thought about the difference within herself since she had returned from Dublin. Certainly the memory of the incredible feelings she had experienced with Adrian had not faded, in fact she considered that they never would, no matter what her path held for her. She was calm, incredibly so given the potentially tumultuous months which lay ahead now that she had articulated the decision to end the marriage so clearly. Life was starting to unfold as a series of wonders as she followed her intuition, her soul's message.

The universe seemed to be teaching her now how to let go, to lose attachments in a manner which presented life-lessons in the smallest of ways. One day she mislaid a ring. This was no ordinary ring. She had bought it on a trip to Edinburgh with girlfriends some six months ago. She had been standing in one of the uppermost turrets of Edinburgh Castle, gazing through the glass window of a promontory to the sprawling buildings that extended out to fill her entire view, when an experience of a distant life came upon her once more. She felt a sudden rush of wind whip around her face. As she momentarily closed her eyes to shield them from the blast, she considered that this was impossible as the turret was completely enclosed.

When she opened her eyes she saw that the glass had disappeared and had been replaced with a shaft that opened out to show green fields that stretched as far as the eye could discern. Louise felt that she was robed in heavy cloth, although she did not see it as her gaze was fixed upon the scene in front of her. After some moments she shut her eyes again and when she opened them once more, all had returned to its original state. Although quite used to these experiences throughout her life, when she came down from the tower she was, without doubt, in an altered space, and drawn as if by some kind of invisible thread, to a cabinet in the lower basement, at the entrance to the shop. This cabinet had only three items for sale, one of which was a ring with a design that entranced her. The ring was forged from metal and enamel, and the design etched onto the ring, 'Skyran', translated as 'blessing on the soul'. This design was a direct copy of an inscription found upon a whorl-stone on the island of Orkney, one of the islands on which the *Book of Kells* was reputedly written. From the moment she bought the ring and placed it on her finger it certainly had that effect upon her! From that moment, she knew that her consciousness had started to shift subtly.

As Louise struggled to find the ring, turning the house upside-down in search of what had become her most precious possession, she felt the heavy weight of its loss, for she knew that it was one of only three that had been available to purchase from the castle, and that the rings were not available anywhere else. She called the castle to see if they could replace it and, after a phone call in which they explained that this was extremely unlikely, sat to contemplate the situation. The blessing on her soul, she determined, was not begotten from the ring but from the universe. It was her belief in this blessing which had been the catalyst for the changes in her, and not the ring itself. Although she had determined to give this ring to her soul-partner one day, knowing that to give something so precious was a true declaration of unconditional love, she must trust in the fact that if it was meant to be, the ring would somehow be found. A couple of days later, the staff at the castle left a message to say that they had managed to find one more of the rings and had posted it to her. But within an hour of receiving this message, Louise found the original ring in a place in which it had certainly not been before! It was because of her trust that she had received twice-fold that which she had thought was lost. This was an important lesson for her to carry forward.

* * *

The day before she was due to leave for Italy Louise had an overwhelming feeling that she should call a man who had been recommended to her by a friend. This man had been a clairvoyant since a young age. As she chatted to this man named Joe, she felt once again the strange sensation of familiarity with the essence of his voice that she had experienced with many lately. Both of them were astounded at the number of messages he was given for her. Many of these, he explained, were not for general consumption, not for the world's knowledge right now. There was much more that he was given, but was told explicitly not to impart to Louise at this time for she, he was told, must come to an understanding of these things for herself. So much was to be made aware to her over time that, if he imparted more than a mere fraction of it now, she would be completely and utterly overwhelmed.

Joe spoke to her of her imminent divorce, of her life dramatically changing around her, and of the fact that right now she could not possibly comprehend what lay ahead of her, but that she must trust the universe to guide her along her path. 'Try all and refuse nothing,' he implored. He spoke of her connection with divinity, of the love and support that surrounded her and of the great importance of what lay ahead of her. He reinforced the message that she must only know now what was appropriate to know. Finally, he spoke of the men to be in her life. He explained that the man she had met in Dublin would come back to her in the future, but not in the capacity that she would imagine. They would somehow work together, and that he was vibrationally at the same level as her. He spoke of another man who was to come to her. This man, he said, would mark a significant change in her future. She would know him – she would recognise his hands, his eyes, and he would have something of an 'X' factor about his personality which she would resonate with entirely.

Louise thanked Joe for his time and, not at all interested at this point in time in pursuing any relationship with another man, what with so much else ahead of her, commenced packing for her family's next trip.

* * *

The following day, Louise arrived in Italy with her three boys. Staying high in the mountains with friends, at a beautiful, ancient village in Tuscany, they whiled away the days with simple food, simple pleasures and deep and meaningful discussion. It was a real sanctuary, hidden from the world-at-large, sacred and truly rejuvenating for the soul. They ventured out only for small pleasures – cray fishing in the mountain streams, trekking through the lush forests, strolling through the medieval village steeped in history at the foot of the mountains, soaking up the ambience.

By the end of the week Louise felt a deep peace, an inner knowing that all was to be well. She would not rush ahead with the separation, leaving a trail of destruction in her wake, but rather she would gently ease everyone through the break-up with the love and compassion that had always been her bedrock. She had waited this long to finally come to a point where she could speak her truth. A few months more, gently manipulating a new life for her family, was surely far more likely to bring things to a calm resolution.

* * *

But back in England, as Louise stepped through the door of her house and reality set in, she began to come to terms with the difficulty of the task that lay ahead. She determined to start the process of parting without delay, and so began the process of discussions to bring this about. She booked herself onto a course in Ireland in October, which had caught her attention before she left for Italy. This was an Angelic Reiki course, and for some reason unbeknownst to her conscious self, she felt driven to attend. She felt sure that there she would find answers to explain the increasing contact she was having with the spiritual beings who surrounded her constantly now. As she spoke to the teacher on the other end of the phone, she knew that her voice, her energy, was not new to her experience. Somehow the lilt of the voice resonated with her; something within her intonation sang familiarity within her.

She arranged to meet the girl, whose name was Floe Magdalena (and who later became affectionately known to Louise as Floe) one lunchtime. While she waited in a coffee bar, Louise felt Floe's energy at the base of the stairs before she had even appeared. She knew, at that moment, what she would look like, how she would act, knew in fact that she was part of her past, her present, her future, her family. And indeed she was. They started chatting as if they had picked up once more upon their discussions across the millennia of time, each knowing what the other was thinking, was about to say. They both knew overwhelmingly that their bond transcended eons of lifetimes, that they shared sister energies, and that they were sisters once more, reunited in perfect divine timing. This was the beginning within this lifetime, of a bond that would form part of the intrinsic change to the very fabric of life, the fabric of humanity's consciousness. These two were, even then, aware of the deep importance of their reunion.

This meeting was, without doubt, a further catalyst for major change within Louise. Somehow her awareness seemed to shift dramatically, as if a release had happened within her very essence. The only experience she could relate this to, was the feeling of electricity she had experienced as a current around her body on different occasions during the summer months. This had seemed always to blow light bulbs, electrical circuits, to quite suddenly halt televisions and DVD players mid-operation. Whilst this feeling was far subtler, it nevertheless had the effect of her viewing everything around her in a slightly altered way.

It was just a week after this meeting that a major new event was to change Louise's life forever. She was shopping in her local supermarket one Friday lunchtime, having just finished speaking to Floe. As she strolled idly along one of the aisles, she was overcome with a knowing to drop what she was doing and walk directly to the checkout. This, she thought, was absurd. She was in no hurry, so why did she feel this sudden urgency? But her intuition was insistently urging her to move right away. She knew by now that she must follow her intuition, her soul's messages, implicitly, and so she walked directly to the checkout.

As she stood in the queue and glanced forward, she noticed a man standing a couple of places ahead of her, with his back towards her. He was tall, with dark, wavy, collar-length hair. Something about him seemed so incredibly familiar to her, but she couldn't quite put her finger on what it was. As she considered for a moment a knowing that he was the reason that she had somehow been compelled to race to the queue, he turned and glanced at her. She looked away. Was that coincidental? This time she spoke with her soul, demanding that if he was indeed the reason she was standing here, if in fact he had called her here with his energy, that he turn and look at her again. Instantly he turned back towards her. She looked away once more, astounded at what was occurring. As she looked down at his hand, she noticed his silver rings. Those hands seemed so familiar to her, but she still couldn't quite place this familiarity, even as he looked directly into her eyes before leaving. Later that night, she recounted the story to her dear friend, Julie. Both dismissed it as yet another of Louise's experiences of late, in which she felt a vague recognition of people she'd never before met.

The very next evening, Louise was driving home late, having taken two of her boys to see a movie. As she drove back along a long and windy country road in the dark of the night, both boys asleep in the back of the car, she quite suddenly had an image of the man she had seen the day before. He was standing in the same queue she had seen him in, but this time he was facing her. She could see his face clearly, he was slightly bearded, and was wearing trousers, a black jacket and scarf, but he looked slightly different from how she had remembered him. Within this vision, he smiled at her. As he did so, the electrics in her car quite suddenly tripped, leaving her with no lights for at least ten seconds. The passenger seat belt indicator started to flash and the alarm bleeped for another five miles or so (even while there was no passenger in the seat). Louise laughed. She somehow suspected that her universal friends were sending her a very unsubtle message. The trouble was, she didn't know what that message was.

* * *

The rest of the weekend passed and when Monday came around, Louise found herself dashing once more into the supermarket, totally distracted with thoughts of work. As she rushed to collect a token for her trolley, she turned around and stopped dead in her tracks. For there, standing in front of her, was the man once more. But this time he was facing her, wearing the exact same clothes and standing in the exact position she had seen him in in her vision. Louise stood, rooted to the spot in a state of disbelief. Somebody tapped her on the shoulder and she turned to speak to them, her mind working in overdrive. What was this all about? But when she turned back, she saw he had gone.

Glancing towards the door, Louise saw the man striding away. Her intuition practically screamed at her to follow him. She almost didn't, considering that she had never followed anybody before in her entire life. And yet, she considered, had she not followed Adrian out of the bar in Dublin? Somehow she knew that now, as then, she must follow her soul's message implicitly. She walked out of the shop, up the slope to the high street, and sped up in an attempt to catch him up as he strode into the Castle Gardens. She reached the tranquillity of the gardens, which she always felt possessed a sense of sacred purpose. Unlike the times that she had sat in these gardens in the past, however, the sense of sacred purpose she felt now seemed directed straight at her.

She glanced around and saw him sitting alone on a bench, eating a sandwich. Although instantly aligned with his need for solitude, a trait that she admired within people, her heart beat faster as she considered what her intuition was telling her to do – to walk right up to him and say something. But how could she do this? It was crazy, and yet she knew it had to be done. Her soul was leading her on an amazing journey and to ignore its instruction was tantamount to destroying that journey.

Louise took a deep breath, walked straight up to him and asked the first thing that came out of her mouth – she asked if he worked around here. It was a crazy thing to say. Louise was usually so articulate, so relaxed and at ease talking to strangers, but on this occasion she was completely flummoxed. What was wrong with her? When he replied 'Yes', Louise said the next crazy thing that came into her head – was it a certain company? He looked completely bemused as, after he replied that no, he didn't work for that company, all she replied was 'fine', and then she walked away.

Sitting on a bench in another part of the garden, completely out of sight, Louise berated her soul. What was going on? Why had she been directed to do this? She sat for a while, writing in her journal until she noticed him walk past and away down the hill in the distance. She felt her soul speak once more, to go and look at the bench where he had been sitting. She knew this was madness but, following her instructions, her body registered shock as she approached the bench, for there, trailing across the grass as if shaping a path, and winding all around the bench where he had been sitting, were about fifty white feathers.

Chapter 5

It was Louise's son's birthday and she and Gillian were sitting in the stalls in Wembley Arena, watching an ice-dancing show with their children. As her thoughts drifted back to their school days, Louise marvelled at the wonder of the universal plan, for these nieces and nephew would always remain family for her, so special to her not only because they were such beautiful children, but also because of the close bond of friendship which had knitted she and Gillian together from such a young age. Louise felt that she had clearly been destined to bring her friend together with her husband's brother; they were so completely at one with each other from the moment they had met. It was now abundantly clear, as she continued the process of separation and divorce from her husband, that she and Gillian were to be close for the entire span of their lifetime. This brought great comfort and joy to her for Gillian was one person in her life who always had, and always would understand her deeply.

As they watched the characters and dancers glide gracefully around the ice, it struck Louise how absorbed the people around the arena were by the spectacle in front of their eyes. The ambience had been set, the lights were bright and the costumes were an array of vibrant colours, the colours of the essence of life: air, sea, fire, in fact, she contemplated, the colours of all the elements of life itself. She started to consider the colours of other civilisations, of blues and silvers, of the colours inherent within different planetary structures and galaxies. The thought fleetingly crossed her mind of the impact that seeing the magnificence of the universe was having on the audience, just as it would have on the consciousness of humanity. Would not that very vision restore humanity's desire to caress and protect both this beautiful jewel of a planet we live on, and the beauty and integrity of the universe?

The moment passed and they spent the rest of the day laughing, enjoying each other's company, and when she went to bed, feeling tired but happy, Louise fell instantaneously into a gentle slumber. She felt as if she had hardly shut her eyes when she woke suddenly, sat up in bed and looked at the clock. The time on the clock read 11.11. All was quiet in the house and, careful not to wake the children, she quietly crept downstairs. Following her intuition, knowing by now that this was her soul giving her direction, and loving the consequences of the directives she had received, Louise picked up a pen and some paper, made herself a drink and, sitting quietly, started to write.

In that moment of awakening, the most incredible thoughts appeared in her head, which she knew were of the utmost importance. Her soul was imploring her to commit these thoughts to paper immediately. Starting to write, she did not know where this was leading, but she continued to repeat the thoughts she heard within her head and visualised in her mind's eye. She was so exhilarated with what was unfolding before her very eyes that she did not notice the hours slipping effortlessly past. As she finally sat back and took in the enormity of what she had just written she realised that she had been writing for six hours, for the time on the clock read 5:55.

She made herself another drink and read, reread and reread once again the almost unbelievable bones of the story that lay written on the pages in front of her. How could she possibly have conceived these words from out of nowhere? But in fact she knew that she had not created them herself, for as she digested what she had written, she realised that many of the details in what she had written, which formed the overall structure of the story, were things she had never before heard of, and that she had no idea what they even meant. There was one thing, however, of which she was entirely sure. This story's central character was she. This was the story of her journey to awakening, her truth and humanity's destiny, and although she couldn't quite believe what seemingly lay before her and the universe within this story, she knew beyond all doubt that it was to happen. This, she understood, was her soul's purpose, her reason for being here in this lifetime, and seeing the enormity of this purpose loom ahead did not overwhelm her in the slightest.

She was full of the deepest sense of peace, joy, excitement and purpose. As she considered the work ahead she knew that she would be pilloried once more (as she was coming to realise she had been in many previous incarnations) for standing up for her truth, for speaking the truth of her soul, the truth of the universe, the knowledge she had brought from eons of lifetimes. For there was no hiding from the truth contained within the pages of this book, from the truth of her journey. Her life was the very basis of, the very reason for, the huge shift to take place within the consciousness of humanity that she had witnessed towards the end of her book. As she considered the way the book had unfolded, she knew beyond all doubt that this book would be hugely successful when published, that it would be made into a highly successful film, and that the proceeds would enable her, just as they had the character in the book, to set up a foundation to put in place the radical changes proposed within the book. These changes were to turn the ethics and morals upon which the current powers of society were operating, on their head. They were to finally bring back the right to the dignity of survival for all. Most importantly they were to propel humanity to a state of heightened consciousness, to a realisation of its destiny, an understanding of who and what we truly are – part of one all-encompassing whole.

Louise knew that to make this happen, this book would need to be read by most of the world in one way or another, that the film would also need to be seen by the entire world's population, and that this was indeed a hugely ambitious goal. She also knew that to release the book as a biography would not achieve its goal. It was imperative that the book should read as a novel, in the same way that other recent books revealing major truths had been released as novels and had been widely read and debated. And it was imperative that it should only contain the truth.

Louise was not daunted by her task. This book had come directly from the universe and through her soul. She knew this was her divine purpose and that she was to co-create this with the universe. As surely as this was the universe's directive, she knew that every person, event, place and piece of information she needed would come to her. She felt stunned as she considered the nature of the people she was to draw to her as pioneers to help her implement these radical changes. These were people to sweep aside governments, and huge world-dominating institutions, and they would be people who, like her, would be unafraid of speaking and living their truth. As she considered the sweeping nature of these changes she delighted in the knowing of the extent of their planetary and ultimately, universal effect. It seemed that every area of life was to be irrevocably changed.

Before her lay the change to the intrinsic basis of life:

- Energy: Every energy source was to be replaced with an alternative one which she had outlined the formulae for, although she had no idea what it actually was. She had described its parameters, character and the scientific processes that would be involved in brief form, outlining the elements to be used in the research and in the application of that research to produce the final product. She had outlined the energy's absolute masculine/feminine balance, using its electromagnetic, crystalline and other properties, which she somehow knew, incredibly seeming to remember, would be in universal harmony.

- Medicine: She had constructed a conceptual model of a kind of health centre incorporating mainstream medicine as a tiny fraction of its overall method. She was already aware of many of the practices she had written about, but several of them she had never heard of. These were practices encompassing the use of the language of light, molecular restructuring, DNA/ascension determinology, audiocleansing, crystalline balancing, lightbody enabling – the list went on and on. These centres were to be established and replicated in their entirety around the globe.

- Schooling: The fundamental basis of schooling was to be turned upon its head. Children would be taught always to work from the basis of inspiration, to understand their purpose. They would be taught that when you follow your purpose, you find yourself a greater person by far than you thought yourself to be. The curriculum Louise had written was tantamount to a heretical taunting of the existing structures. She, however, was overwhelmed with a wonderful feeling of knowing that this was indeed the liberation of one's very self, the path to utter wisdom and the bliss of life.

- Media – Publishing/News/Television/Film: These changes were radical indeed. The world must understand the inspirational truth in all things. The spirit of enquiry and freedom of expression and truth must be kept alive in times when these very virtues seemed to be under threat. Louise had written out an entirely new programme of development. This eradicated the bureaucracy in place right now, which prevented just such expression, and repositioned all to give them the right to express their message, their truth. An entirely new approach would provide all with the opportunity to publish books, submit news, enlighten and enhance film and other media production. Most importantly, the inspiration in all was to be the paramount message of the entire media presentation. When the population at large was inspired, and began to act upon its inspiration and love, so would its consciousness and reality become that inspiration and love.

- Single World Federation: All 160 world nation states were to unite under a single world federation. This federation's sole purpose was to ensure that the basic right to dignity and survival for all was established. The challenge would be not to make everyone equal, but to give everybody the assurance of a life lived with dignity, and to allow all to choose their path from that point. A huge shift of consciousness was aligned with the new political practices to be installed. This shift was universal truth – that nothing is separate from anything else. Everything is intrinsically connected, utterly bound, interactive and interwoven into the fabric of life. All politics must be based upon this truth. All laws must be rooted in it, as this is the only hope for the future of this race and planet. All money currently spent on defence and attack systems was to be redirected to create homes, health and employment around the world. A true visionary was to emerge, one who would value all of these principles, whose monetary policy would specifically aid those with business potential, but no collateral, and who would support in entirety the empowerment of both women and men in absolute balance.

- Music: Music was to become instrumental within every element of daily life. It would underpin media presentation, schooling, healing and many other practices, the likes of which she had never heard of. She wrote about principles where the healing vibrations of music would be used to change the discordant and conflicting vibrations that cause disease. Music was to be re-understood as the language of feeling, and feeling the language of the soul.

- Communications Technologies: Although the Internet had already established a certain level of access to information, Louise envisioned an avenue to truth for all, giving the power truly to the people. She was astounded at the redefinition of communications laid out before her now. For here was the methodology to truly empower every last person upon this planet. She had written about things such as online virtual reality games advocating the search for one's purpose and the pursuit of inspiration that were to be established. Through other teachings, highly enhanced practices would be re-established within the psyche of all, to enable telecommunication via telepathy and other ancient practices.

- Research Centres: Scientific research centres were to be established which would bring together science and spirituality, with noetics as their base. These would specifically work towards a greater understanding of the universe, targeting the essence of energy as oneness and determinedly reinstating ancient lost studies and practices, in order to harmoniously enhance all areas of life. These centres would be positioned in accordance with energy vortexes – areas where the very fabric of life had been gently teased apart many eons ago.

- Religion: Conference centres were to be established globally, bringing together the understanding of science and spirituality, providing all with the ability to understand the intrinsic nature of our being, our energetic source, our inter-relationship with the planet, the universe, and beyond. All people would be brought to an awareness and understanding of the common thread of the message of oneness which runs throughout organised religions, and would learn that, in fact, our relationship with the universe, the divine, with God, transcends all organised religion, and is in fact a relationship with the divine, the universe itself. This message of oneness was of course the basis of the harmony of the universe, love and balance.

- Weather: A far greater affinity was to be drawn with the operations of the weather. Astral weather was to become the determining factor in scheduling events of a planetary nature, of setting into motion new realities and intentions.

And so the list went on. Louise was being shown, very clearly, a thread of light that seemed to form an enormous grid overlaying the entire globe. Knitted within this grid of light were people, those people she was to draw together to form the basis of these changes. She wasn't entirely sure that she would know how to draw these pioneers together, but she did know beyond any doubt that if this were what the universe intended, they would start to appear.

* * *

For the rest of that day Louise was completely and utterly preoccupied with the thoughts that were immersing her consciousness. She felt a sense of total purpose and knew that she was at the beginning of a truly amazing journey, her journey, her soul's purpose.

All that filled her being was a sense of longing to write. It was as if she understood that a valve within her inner knowledge, eons of knowledge, had just been opened. It was so strange. She considered that she had never harboured a desire of any kind to write. She had always been an avid reader, enjoyed literature and prose but never once had she considered the notion of writing. But now, transcribing all that poured forth from within was all that Louise could do.

Chapter 6

Over the next couple of weeks Louise kept bumping into the man she had met in the supermarket, often a trail of feathers once more leading a path to him. Every time she saw him she felt that tug of familiarity, of knowing of some deep connection between them, and yet she could not quite place him. She knew that this feeling was reciprocated for she saw him watching her when he thought she wasn't looking. He would stand right by her in a queue, his body language displaying the evidence of his curiosity. When one day she felt compelled to ask him if he was a journalist, convinced that somehow he had been sent to help her with her book, he just smiled shyly and said no.

The time had come for her to travel to Ireland for her Angelic Reiki course. She and her by now inseparable friend, Floe, talked with conviction and without hesitation across the entire journey. The only time they stopped was to entertain a charming man, quite clearly in need of bathing in their energies for the duration of the flight. The course was a further turning point for Louise for, during those few days she finally came to know implicitly all of the beings that had been surrounding her for all of this time. She learnt to recognise, visualise and differentiate the energies of the masters, the angelic realm and the multidimensional beings that came forward within the healings.

It was on the second day, while being asked to complete an absent healing, that she began to understand the connection she had felt with the man she had continued to meet in town. Directed by her soul's notion, she commenced a healing for him. This was strange when so many people would have been uppermost in her mind to send healing to. As she visualised him sitting on that same bench with his back to her in the castle gardens, they quite suddenly were transported to a large, dark room. This room was illuminated by a circle of candles and they were inside the centre of the circle. As the healing progressed he turned to her, tears streaming down his face, clearly displaying grief. This grief tore at her heart, tore at the very core of her essence and in that moment she understood that this pain was both hers and his. This was the pain of a wrenching apart, of two people so close, so undeniably part of one another, and with this pain came an overwhelming sensation of nausea. The nausea became acute, along with a searing pain, which streamed through the crown of her head and ran down through her throat, amplifying the intense feeling of nausea.

As the healing drew to a close, Louise was wracked with these feelings, both physical and emotional. While all the others in the group completed a self-healing, she could barely move, she felt so incredibly grief-stricken and in such pain. She rushed up to her room to be violently sick, then lay on the bed, unable to move in even a tiny manner. After an hour or so, Floe came and sat gently on the edge of the bed, understanding her friend's desperate condition. She asked what had happened and as Louise explained, under Floe's direction, she quite suddenly drifted once more into a previous existence.

This time she could see herself dressed in a long white robe, drowning under a blanket of white water. It was as if she were reaching up towards the top of a long funnel of rushing water, desperately trying to reach an outstretched hand above her, but not being able to grab it. This was his hand, and in those moments she understood that she was not in the least bit frightened of the concept of dying, but her heart was torn asunder at the thought of losing this man she loved so. As her friend directed her to remove the pain etherically from the areas within her body where she felt this grief, and to replace it with feelings of love, an incredibly light sensation flooded her entire being. She stood, slightly unbalanced on her feet, but entirely free of any pain or nausea. As she looked in the mirror it was as if her skin radiated, shone with the love that was theirs. She knew then that, upon her return to England, she must speak to Him.

* * *

The course concluded with the attunement ceremony in which the blessings and gifts of the angelic realm were bestowed upon the participants. In a meditative state of complete wakefulness they entered the final ceremony where, having received the master crystal, they were to travel beyond many dimensions to the great white pyramid to receive their attunement and gifts.

As they travelled through many tunnels of light, vivid colours passed by at speed. They traversed many dimensions, crossing through the Void as they passed from one tunnel and dimension to the next. Symbols and shapes of varying size, colour and detail, appeared as they traversed. The healing symbols all seemed so familiar to Louise, images from Atlantis flooding back.

They came to the top of a great white pyramid, so vast that its base covered the entire sphere of Louise's vision. They flew in through the top of the pyramid and down to its base. In the centre were three columns of light which changed shape to take on the appearance of something more resembling human form as they approached. These three great angels welcomed them, one by one, accompanied by thirty-two angels who all came forward with their individual gifts of wisdom, love and knowledge, bestowing them upon each person in their own individual way, attuning their master crystal at the same time.

Louise stood in wonder and awe at the love and beauty that surrounded her. She felt so humbled and glorious in that instant. It was as if she were standing in the midst of the most glorious and mighty creations of the universe, and yet felt as if she'd come home. As Archangel Azrael presented her with the gifts of the Merkaba, gently touching her forehead, every essence of her being trembled with exhilaration. She was exalted. Her intuition told her to turn around, and when she looked behind she saw a staggeringly beautiful sight, a tunnel of pure white crystal, emanating a blinding white light. At the end of the tunnel stood a crystal altar and on it, a very large, very old, tattered brown leather book. She felt so drawn to this book, she knew the intention was for her to take it, read it and assimilate the information within. But the ceremony had finished, and it was imperative that they leave now.

The others were flying up through the pyramid's ceiling. If she took the book and stayed she might not be able to find her way back. She so longed to read it, knowing it was her gift. Intuitively however, she started to ascend with the others, somehow knowing that the contents of the book would reach her, and as she came to the summit and was about to leave, she felt the gentle touch of Archangel Uriel's hand upon her head, his other hand bound tightly to the book. As this beautiful angel's hand touched her head she felt a sudden rush of understanding flood her senses. All the knowledge contained within this book was within her. She had only to find the keys to unlock the inner wisdom held within her own labyrinth of knowledge, and the universe would then assist the flow of information.

She came back with the others, through all dimensions at speed, until finally, she looked down upon her body and entered it once more. As her body came out of its meditative state, she began to weep with joy and humility, feeling the heaviness of being back once again in physical form, and not wanting to leave that glorious place. As they discussed their individual experiences, she came to learn that the book had been the *Book of Enoch*, incorporating the wisdom of all ages. It had been presented to her symbolically so that she might understand and trust that in writing her book, all the knowledge she needed would be brought back to her, unlocked from within. She needed now to ensure that she clear all blockages that would prevent the wisdom from being accessed. She needed to dedicate time to unlocking the wisdom of her soul. The steps would, as ever, be presented to her in perfect timing.

* * *

As she strolled through town the following week, Louise grabbed some lunch and headed off up to the castle gardens to write once more, her thoughts preoccupied with a sense of profound understanding that was soon to be unveiled. Sitting quietly, soaking up the ambience of these sacred grounds, she looked up to see him walk past her. As she jumped to her feet, he looked across and smiled at her. She walked to him and, introducing herself, asked if he wanted to grab a coffee and chat. He was rushing back to work in a hurry and had no time, but smiled, took her hand and introduced himself in a deep Australian accent, as Ben. He dashed off down the hill, smiling at her as he left. As she sat on the bench, considering the brief encounter, she closed her eyes. The wind blew gently against her cheeks, the sun softly caressed the crown of her head, and she drifted into a meditative state. Within her meditation she was transported back to an image of a previous existence, and quite suddenly it all came flooding back, bringing with it acute emotions.

A podium stood before her and tall, majestic stone pillars rose on all sides, while drapes of blue gauze blew gently around the pillars in the breeze. She walked up many steps to reach the podium. The colours all about her were blue and silver, the essence of air, the sea, the breath of life, the passion for the love of a civilisation not lost. It was the image of a new age coming, of cool waters, endless depths of emotion, staggering beauty and heavens opened. The eternal promise of clarity, love, time and the revelation of what the entire universe had to offer. In the distance she could see waves lapping gently against white shores.

As she stepped up, He took her hand, the hand of a priestess clothed in blue gauze, a circlet of silver in her hair and a white quill in her other hand. Together they walked through the drapes wafting gently in the breeze and he took her to the stone altar. There, He laid his hand on her forehead while she anointed his with sacred oils. They looked upon one another, every essence of their souls entwined with the other's, for this was a sacred Atlantean union, bound for time eternal. She laid Him gently on the altar and began to lay chakra crystals lovingly on each of his chakra centres, his robe falling around his waist as she did so. In this sacred moment, the beautiful sounds of ritual music consumed all their senses. While He lay in meditation, she leant forward and gently caressed his lips with her energy. Lifetimes of love engulfed Him, those that had been, that which was here in the present and those which were to come. She summoned all the symbols to her and watched as in mid-air, they danced brightly to her call. She called upon the crystals, set in a pyramid around the altar, to work with her and with the light, and she asked Archangel Metatron to overlight this ceremony and bring forward beings of one hundred percent pure light, in order to infiltrate every part of the soul of this man lying before her. Her soul danced and she knew, as surely as she knew that she was one with the universe, that her love would be bound to this man across the entire time-space continuum. As she helped Him to his feet, He took her hand again and felt the physical energy of their touch melt within the power of their entwined souls.

They stepped down from the altar, took whites robes and dressed each other, and each took a tall staff of silver, decorated with a thistle shape at the top. They walked back to the top of the podium and stood to face one other, interlinking their arms and staffs. Another priestess of great dark beauty, her sister, appeared and smiled down upon them. Behind her was a tall blonde man of striking beauty. As she sang the words of the ceremony to bind them together before the universe and across all time, all else faded for them with the exception of her words and her beautiful voice.

He took her face in his hands and looked deep into her soul through her dark eyes. He had surely been given the greatest gift to treasure by the universe. They walked together in complete harmony, down through the heavens it seemed, to a place in a clearing of staggering and mystical beauty. Long silver-leafed trees lopped gently over a bubbling natural spring, which formed an enormous sunken bath. Surrounded by moonlight and hundreds of illuminated candles within the trees, the spring cascading down around them from all directions, they stepped into the bath, still robed. They looked at one another, each understanding every nuance of the other, both mesmerised by this moment and their mutual love. For this was a love beyond the physical. Every part of their soul, every chakra was consumed with the combined sacred energy that was them.

Louise knew, as He had told her many times, that His hand would be hers throughout time. She had told Him that she had a very important task to complete in the future, one that involved writing and would only be possible by revealing the truth of her soul, something for which she knew she was to be persecuted through the ages to come. The universe would reveal the task to her when the time was right. He took her face in his hands once more and looked deep into her eyes. 'Know this, I will find you across all time and space, and when the time comes, I will be there with you so that you will not face the world alone. If you find me in this other lifetime, and I don't remember, never give up on me. Find a way to make me take your face in my hands so that I may look upon your soul and know you once more. As surely as we are bound in love to one another before the universe now, so shall the universe bind us to this troth.'

When she woke from her meditation, Louise's face was sodden with tears, her heart filled with pain and love of remembrance of that moment in time. She slowly walked back to her car and sat in silence for the hours that were hers, those precious moments that instilled her soul's message. And she thought about all that was.

* * *

That night, as she lay in bed and completed a self-healing once more, trying to make sense of all that was happening to her now, the moon called to her. She scaled a stairway through the black of the night to rest at the foot of the moon's gaze. As she beheld the beauty before her, for she so admired and loved the moon, the moon returned her smile. With great joy and peace filling her senses, she explained to the moon how Her beauty inspired her, guided her, and how she felt so honoured to be standing in Her beautiful presence. The moon gently bestowed Her love upon Louise. She smiled and said that it was She who was honoured to be in Louise's presence, that She loved her so, and that her beauty radiated all that was the love of the universe. Louise, so humbled, asked what it was that the moon had been trying to say to her for so long now. For her entire life she had gazed at the moon, watching Her whisper things inaudible, uninterpretable, and which had become much more insistent in their direction over these last months. The moon gazed down upon her, smiled and replied, 'You are my golden child, this I have been telling you for as long as you have ever gazed upon me, and now I have a very great sense of pathos in being able to finally, in this lifetime, tell you.' With tears of joy, of humility and a deep sense of being held, Louise slept deeply through that night, wondering what the universe truly had in store for her. For she had a deep knowing that far more than what was apparent to her now was to be revealed.

* * *

That single act of spontaneous regression that came to Louise in such detail, seemed to precipitate the opening of floodgates from that moment on. Beyond time and space, the memories started flooding back: life after life of passion, abandon, longing, hope, fear, driven always to the goal of pursuing the divinity of the self, and of opening a path through the blinkered vision of humanity and its spiritual destiny.

Ever mindful of the longing for a rekindling of her sacred union from Atlantis, and with the knowledge that he would return, Louise knew that the universe would hold their troth true. She felt his energy with her now, approaching closer daily, and knew that her task for the universe was clear. This book must be written quickly; time was of the essence. She was a scholar in her heart and had always been so. Lifetimes of persecution showed the depth of the maltreatment and torture she had encountered as a result of speaking and writing her truth. These lay alongside lifetimes where she had been highly esteemed for her scholarly talents and inner wisdom.

Indeed, in the court of King Arthur she had been the Wise Woman. All came to her for her clear-thinking abilities, her proclivity for decisive action and because she was the source for universal answers. She had been an alchemist in every sense of the word. She had been held in high esteem in the Spanish courts as a scholar to a Spanish Ambassador in the period of the Armada. She was one of the chief scribes in the Roman court of Julius Caesar, loved and revered, but eventually denounced as a heretic for her strident declarations of divine instruction from the universe. The Romans had loved her, but the Church was threatened. Endless replays and knowing of lives spent in celibacy, in honour and pursuit of the divine word in its purest form as a priestess in the temples of Isis, Delphi and as an oracle, played themselves in Louise's head. There were so many coming back to her now, it was as if her very essence was saturated with the depth of emotions in all things.

Her thoughts always drifted back to those heady days of Atlantis, where life and the universe were intrinsically bound. Life was love and love was life. Always, she remembered dancing and playing with her crystals, running up and down the stone steps to the temple, the wind gently blowing her priestess's veil, the sun catching the light of her circlet, and the laughter and love of her sister chasing her as she ran. The crystals sang to her call, danced to her instruction, the music of life filling her every sense. How she longed for this earth to return to that heady bliss.

* * *

But the time had now come for her to reveal her truth in this lifetime. It was the turn of the times. The tide of humanity's awareness was changing and she must no longer fear persecution for what she knew to be the truth. She had chosen to hide her truth until now, albeit subconsciously, with a knowing that the true light and wisdom of her soul needed to be revealed at the precise divine timing. All the knowledge and wisdom that needed to be within the pages of her book was within her soul. The keys to unlock the information had been given to her and she was thirsty for more and more ways to reveal the truth rooted deep within her.

Never had she felt more exhilarated, impassioned, dedicated or moved. Nor had she ever experienced such a wonderful inner peace. Every moment of every day was a wondrous gift in which she marvelled at the magnificence of the universe around her. She was never alone, with constant messages surrounding her in the animals, trees, sun, moon, her guides, angels and masters, ever constant in their attention and loving presence. She felt their energy hold her hand, stroke her face, lovingly caress her hair, filling her body with the sense of all the love of her soul, tidal waves of feeling rising within. Life was a fabulous journey of rediscovery of the universe and of the self, and the more of herself that came through, the more she realised that her knowledge and wisdom was vital now to humanity's destiny. Her mind having been opened, and the whole story given to her to write, Louise now implored the universe to bring everything and everyone to her quickly, to assist in unlocking all the information she needed to write this book in full.

And the universe obliged, lovingly, willingly, in a state of delight and laughter at its golden child's final return to love, light and consciousness. The more Louise implored, the more the universe provided. Miracles amazed her daily, as she literally bumped into people, discovered places, events and situations that constantly helped to unlock the wisdom within. As her book started to unfold before her eyes, she was staggered as she read back the knowing held within its covers, the wonderful audacity with which her truth was hitting the pages. Moved by its emotion, the truth of the experience of her soul over the eons, she knew that the changes about to unfold and grip the world as a result of the publication of her book, would indeed happen.

Deep within her soul, Louise knew that she had only to reach out to the universe with all the joy and laughter brought about by the knowledge of the help it would send her in the form of influential people who would assist her. She knew that they would start to emerge. And gradually, they did.

Chapter 7

A few weeks after her return from Ireland saw Louise rapt with anticipation, for she was taking part in a day course given by Cherry, to understand the ancient use of crystals. Cherry was an amazing lady, well-educated across the breadth of all that was so in tune with the universal dictum, who had been introduced to Louise through a friend as someone who could truly help her now as her knowledge and path progressed. Louise had visited her many times now to receive a form of Tera Mai Seichem reiki. Every time they were together, many messages were passed to Louise through the healings, several of which released specific keys and codes from her days in Atlantis. She and Cherry knew them to be accurate, for almost every time, they received identical messages simultaneously.

This day's healing was particularly apposite as, having read so many books now about the ancient civilisations of Atlantis and Lemuria, Louise knew that today would be a day to release yet more keys and codes within her. She had read about these civilisations dating back to 50,000 BC, and the significance of the date, alongside her absolute knowing, made her sure that the things she learnt today would contribute fundamentally to her reality now. Somehow she felt this day ahead would give her glimpses of more of her past. As she sat in anticipation of the knowledge she would learn that day, she felt the presence of the crystals laid out in front of her, calling her, teasing her, playing with her. This felt so reminiscent of a lifetime long ago. These crystals were her companions. They had danced with her, healed for her, been bound to a sacred union with her. What would they reveal to her today? Would they indeed open her chakras to offer yet another glimpse of promise?

As she began to listen to the information that was being divulged to her, Louise understood all that was being told to her, as if she were being reminded, and not shown for the first time. She was being reminded of the kinetic, pyro- and piezoelectric energy properties of the crystals. She remembered how important their use had been in providing a clean and abundant energy source for the civilisation. She recalled that they were parts of a key hub which had siphoned the conscious knowledge of every citizen of Atlantis to provide a hub of astonishing proportions of energy.

Louise learnt that seven crystal skulls had been kept in Atlantis. The energies that lived within these skulls had far greater capacity than computers of today. These skulls contained universal knowledge, secrets from Atlantis. Most had been broken during the destruction of the civilisation, but rumour had it that at least one of them still existed, and was stored somewhere in the world today. She was astonished to learn that Hitler had considered himself the pioneer who would rebuild

Atlantis, and that he had been searching for the crystal skulls as he believed that he was breeding a race of children that would recreate Atlantis. His thirst for the knowledge contained within these skulls was fired by his belief that once he owned this knowledge he would possess universal power. This of course was misguided, as crystals and their energies (crystal devas) choose their owners and would only allow knowledge to be channelled from them if they wished it.

Louise remembered how in Atlantis, crystals had been used to increase concentration, to intensify psychic/spiritual ability, for healing, schooling and meditation, as well as providing astounding energy sources. As she saw the Atlantean crystal healing symbol before her, in preparation for the performance of a crystal cleansing ceremony, thoughts of the many times she had used this symbol came flooding back.

Together this group now built four-sided healing crystal pyramids, each in the group taking turns to either build the pyramid, or to sit within it to receive the incredible downpouring of healing from its top apex. As she sat within her pyramid many images flashed past, as if a slide-show of a life long past. She felt the very essence of her past energies flooding back.

Finally the time had come to do the chakra-balancing, using the crystals. As she laid her partner out and started to lay the crystals along her chakras, the girl in front of her quite literally transformed before her very eyes. In her place she saw Him once more, robed from the waist down in a white gauze robe. She knew with every essence of her being, and with painful and yet deeply moving recollection of that sacred Atlantean ceremony, that she had performed chakra-balancing on him many times. Lovingly, tenderly, she started to do what came flooding back to her. The crystals danced and their sweet tune rang in her ears. The joy and love of the past overwhelmed her senses. When the balancing had completed, she felt somewhere between rapturous joy and deep grief. It was her turn to lie down. As she closed her eyes and entered the meditative state she instinctively knew she must take, she felt His overwhelming presence with her. She knew it to be Him, she remembered every nuance of his movements, his energy and as He leaned forward and caressed her face, her heart chakra exploded, her chest pulsating with energy. She wept within, longing for the time when they would be reunited, for in those moments the remembrance of the intensity of their sacred union was beyond all expression and thought. It was divine.

As she searched for answers within, teachers around her assured her that she had been seeing images of work she was doing with Him on the etheric plane, work that was preparing them both for the time soon approaching when they would be together again. She had seen so many visions of late, always where she was guiding him back to remembrance, taking flight with him, reassuring him, loving him. As the day came to a close she understood the importance that the crystals must have in her book as providers, not only of clean energy sources, but also as great healing aids, companions and containers of knowledge.

* * *

The following day, escaping from the madness of work to grab lunch and seek the tranquillity of the castle gardens, Louise bumped into him once more. They chatted idly about his work and other things, and she looked him directly in his eyes as they both smiled. She explained that she was writing a book, an intriguing book, and that she had been so sure that her intuition had guided her to him to help her with it. Although she clearly understood that there must be much more to their relationship, as he so resembled the image of the man she was seeing so often now in her past, she was still trying to piece together the threads as they presented themselves to her in this reality. What was this union to be about? But he explained that he was not involved in book publishing in any capacity. They chatted and laughed a little longer until she finally left him standing there, once again looking bemused.

A couple of days later he was strolling past her once more, striding out across the castle gardens on a cold and windy day, but she only noticed him as she heard laughter, and looked up to see him laughing at her as she spilled her drink. They laughed and joked so comfortably in each other's company and, as he rushed back in the direction of work, they teased each other. He joked about needing to rush back, she chided him for feeling he needed to rush back. She told him that he needed to stop rushing, to chill out! As he disappeared into the distance, laughing and waving goodbye, her intuition told her to give him a favourite CD of hers. This was a Tibetan music CD, one that seemed to provoke profound depths of knowledge when she listened to it during meditations or healings. She resolved to buy him a copy, and to give it to him the next time she saw him. She would do so, accompanied with a note explaining that he needed to slow down, to listen to the music and see the doors the universe was trying to open for him.

* * *

The following weekend, Louise was off on a trip to Rome with some friends. Leaving behind the bitterly cold English weather, she truly welcomed the sun that nurtured her face as she stepped off the plane in Rome. The first day was spent idly roaming around the shops, taking in the sights, eating, laughing, drinking and watching the Italian world pass by. On the second day torrential rain meant that the girls wanted to stay inside, and so they headed to the Vatican City. As they approached St Peter's Church, her friends keen to venture inside, Louise felt incredibly uneasy, as the foundations of the Catholic Church were built upon the stronghold of men and not upon the acceptance of the divine feminine and masculine combined. However, she knew beyond any doubt that there was a reason why she had to go in.

The energies deep within the vaults bothered her. While the rest of the world believed their intention to be pure, Louise knew there were many secrets hidden in these vaults. She asked Archangel Michael to protect her from any negative energies she might encounter, and asked to be able to use this experience to receive further enlightenment. Looking around the church, feeling dwarfed by the height of the ceilings, the magnificent stone pillars and porticos, all examples of man's attempts to glorify God in the magnificence of stone and mortar, she realised the true reason behind her presence there. As she gazed upon the infamous 'Pieta' statue of Jesus in the arms of his mother, Mary, Louise felt a deep sadness at the Church's total lack of acknowledgement of the intensity of the love between the twin souls of Jesus and Mary Magdalene. Here in this, the most important house of God for the Catholic Church, one of the greatest loves of all time had been swept away, hidden from all when it should have been celebrated and revered in honour of two individuals who had put the love of the universe above their own. This was a clear example to all the peoples of the universe of love, light and compassion. Mary Magdalene's love for Jesus ran so deeply, that she understood that the importance of his path went beyond his love for her, and that his was the path to tread for the love of the divine, and for all the people of the universe. She had to let Him go, knowing that he would relinquish life in the physical, leaving her. It was the knowledge that their love transcended any boundaries of time and space that enabled her to let go of Him, trusting in their ultimate love to be bound together for eternity.

As Louise pondered this, choking with emotion at the depth of the love and despair that Mary Magdalene must have felt, she suddenly understood why she had been brought to this church. A moment of knowing, so deep, so intense and painful, entered her consciousness. For she understood in that moment that this would indeed be the path she would follow with her twin soul. In coming to her He would bring to the fore that sacred union, the troth they had pledged across time and space, which had been held true by the universe. And she also knew intuitively that their time together would not span this entire lifetime, and that in her love for Him, she would have to let him go.

Only when she knew she would be able to do this, lovingly and willingly, could the universe allow Him to enter her physical life now. Leaving her would not be easy for Him, for He would love no other, the strength of their union going beyond all things. Everything within his world would pale in comparison to her light. But He, like her, had pledged his agreement to complete a very important task for the universe, one that would take Him away from her. Without her strength and direction He would not be able to do that. He would not want to do that and would be at risk of not fulfilling his soul's purpose. Once he had found her, his treasured gift, his life, He would not wish to leave her again. She knew that she would be his strength, and that she would direct Him and love Him beyond all things. For that reason alone she would be able to send Him to complete his oath.

Now Louise finally understood that only when she could truly believe that she would do this with absolute love for Him and the universe, would He properly take his place in her life. She wept, for she knew that she had to accept this loss before even receiving the gift of his return. She must endure the grieving now so that the point at which He would leave her would be a joyous celebration of the fulfilment of his journey. She knew that He would weep, deeply and painfully, as she had already seen this in their future. It was the pain of his weeping that had caused her heart to ache so badly. She knew that, like Mary Magdalene, she would have to trust in their reunion within universal time and space once again. She now knew that every moment of every day, of every month, of every year she was to have with Him would be blessed beyond heaven and earth.

They would have one foot on the earth plane and one foot in the astral plane, intrinsically bound, irrevo-cably pledged to one another, connected at all levels with a depth of love rarely seen on this earth. Their connection would run far deeper than the physical, drawing them together in body, mind and spirit, while they were together and while they were apart. It was with this knowledge that she learnt to accept the time they were to have apart, for she knew that they would always be together, across all lives, all dimensions, all realities. They had pledged themselves to one another in sacred union in the eyes of the universe all those lifetimes ago, and the universe would hold this pledge true for all time.

Now, with these thoughts uppermost in her consciousness, Louise gazed once more upon the statue and understood that this beautiful piece of art, so expertly and intuitively sculpted by Michelangelo, was not a depiction of Jesus with his mother Mary. It was in fact a representation of Jesus in the arms of his lover, his sacred partner, Mary Magdalene, and she knew that the great master Michelangelo had known this as he had created this tribute to their love. Louise hid her face from all around her and wept silently, the acceptance of these things flooding her every sense. Her heart ached as all around her, awe-struck people walked in harmony with the sweet music accompanying mass. Leaving the church with her friends, the weight of her understanding fell heavy upon her shoulders.

Lying in her bed that night, Louise could not sleep. She lay awake for hours, considering the great truths of love which had been hidden for so long, and which surely now it was the right of the people to know about. She considered how many had been wronged by history in its portrayal of their lives, for surely the greatest deeds of love were often those most misaligned to general perception. She considered Judas Iscariot. Here was one of the most misrepresented people of history. Surely now people should truly understand that the very essence of his deep and undeniable love for Jesus was the very strength that enabled him to carry out one of the hardest tasks any person could be forced to complete. For only in true love, trust and honour was he able to complete the task that Jesus had requested of him. His apparent betrayal of his dear friend was, in fact, the demonstration of the very depth of his love. In his kiss he facilitated the manner in which Jesus was able to lay a trail of light for the world to follow. It was time now for those dear friends to be held in honour and loved for their unwavering trust and love.

* * *

The day she arrived home from Rome, weary and utterly drained emotionally, she bumped into Ben once more. On this particular day, the pain of her experience in St Peter's Church still so recent, she truly did not wish to speak to him. But this was the week before Christmas, she had the CD and a short note in her bag, and she knew she would not be in town again to give it to him until after Christmas. She walked up to him, gave him the CD, and told him to accept it, to do what it said within the note, and then she walked away, leaving him with a smile on his face.

Louise felt an overwhelming heaviness within her heart. Still she tried to understand what was going on here. Every time she saw Ben she was drawn more and more to him, his quirky style, his unkempt dark hair, his manner and his beautiful, knowing smile, were all so reminiscent of her sacred partner. Today, wrapped up for winter, he seemed particularly endearing. She, however, desired only solitude and, knowing that the school holidays and Christmas festivities loomed ahead, used this one last chance to seek solace in the gardens. She sat in the bitter wind and allowed the elements to infuse her being with vitality. A profound understanding entered her consciousness, that she was at one with nature and that, somehow, the seasons, the elements themselves, were entirely in tune with her journey now. With that, she understood that the time was now here for a period of great change.

Chapter 8

The next week Louise embarked upon her first series of lightbody surgeries, marking without doubt a period of significant change for her. Lightbody surgery was a method of removing obstacles and barriers to divinity, of completing vow breaks and removing all other etheric devices put in place within our energy fields, to ensure that we come into this reality, playing the game of separation. For, it was explained to her, only by playing the game of separation for a period of time are we truly able to understand the human experience and embrace our path as we become one with its knowing.

This lightbody process was to enable more of Louise's higher self, her enlarged energy field, to be present within her consciousness now. This would bring the ever-increasing flow of knowledge bombarding her consciousness now to even greater heights of clarity and focus, and at greater speed. During the sessions, lifetimes of persecution became ever more evident in her auric energy fields as deep wounds from the lash of whips became evident across her body. Deep scar-like scabs appeared in streaks across her back in the days following her lightbody surgery. These wounds were, Floe explained, the release through Louise's cellular system of the entire trauma of the persecution she had carried with her for so long.

* * *

New Year's Eve came around and, unusually, Louise, found herself with some moments alone. The house was completely silent and she welcomed the brief respite from the seasonal festivities. Although laughter and fun had filled the house, for the children delighted in the mystique of Christmas and she had always ensured they experienced just that, this Christmas period had been so hard. Hard for her and hard for her husband. He was slowly trying to come to terms with the separation ahead and she had wanted to give him this time for acceptance. She felt it only right that a period of calm be instated in order to try to create a path ahead that would be as harmonious as possible for all of them. Still she yearned for the day to come when they could, finally, be apart. Only then could she be free within her own space to allow the energy of the universe to infuse her with all that was to come. She felt sure, especially after so many confirmations of late, that 2007 was to hold the key to her future, her soul's path. She knew that as these last hours represented the closing of a chapter in her past, so the days ahead would be the start of the life to come, the mark of her journey's future.

She started to read from some of her many books, for her hunger for knowledge never was, never had been, and never could be sated, and she considered the words within a book called *Conversations with God.*

What god wants.

What if we've got it all wrong?

What if what god wants is nothing?

Reading these words, Louise intuitively knew that the suggestion in the final question was indeed correct. She had somehow always known this to be true. And if God wants nothing, as the author, Neale Donald Walsh explained, then every model the human race has ever built its ethics and morals upon, must be wrong. All these models were based upon the assumption that all life is lived on a quid pro quo basis. But how could that ever have been? How could God, the universe, life itself, desire anything in return for the existence of itself? If God is life and life is God then we are all part of God, and it is impossible that we would ever not be part of God. When examined under a microscope, everything within this universe is moving energy, even inanimate objects. These are all part of life itself. Part of God. Nothing exists outside of God. What God wants for us is only what God is, and God is everything that there is, and therefore, wants for nothing.

Louise had never believed that a compassionate and loving god would insist upon being obeyed, and damn all to purgatory that did not obey. The idea was preposterous. In fact, she had never believed that purgatory existed. She believed that it was actually a state created by humans to support the structures they put in place to control the masses. They wanted the people to believe that God would damn them to hell should they follow a path not of its choosing. It really quite suited some of these institutions as it enabled them to claim some sort of ordained power, sent by God. But why would God, the universe, wish to assert part of itself against another part of itself? It was an idea based upon the premise that we are all separate from God, and this was something Louise had never believed. She understood the dark side to be the collected negative thoughts arising from human beings living in a state of fear. If fear were eradicated from people's consciousnesses, so would be the ability to create the very images of that fear. The dark would quite simply disappear. Louise had always believed that God's/the universe's desire would be for all to live in the physical as a unique expression of itself and, in a way which allowed the magnificence of life to radiate through every moment of every day, for love and light to be abundant in all around us. This was based upon the premise that we are all part of the same energy force, and there is no separation of us, who are this energy. Louise considered that you have only to look at the discoveries being made by scientists and quantum physicists to prove that this was true.

Even the great masters, those upon whom major world religions had been based, had always insisted that we are all part of the same energy force that is God, the universe. Louise knew that many texts, including the Gnostic texts, interpreted Jesus' comments that He and His father were one, and that when He died He was going to meet with Him, as Jesus referring to his return to the higher essence of Himself, his soul essence, which is one and the same energy as the universe.

When she started to consider the implications of this properly, Louise finally understood that all of the changes she had been writing about were of course based upon the premise of all things being part of one energy source, the universe, and that they were indeed based upon the need to turn the planet's current ideals and morals on their head. This was the only way that mankind could consciously and radically move back towards living in harmony. To continue on its current path would be to allow the devastating destruction of our civilisation, just as had happened all those lifetimes ago in Atlantis. Whether the existing world population chose to believe in the existence, and subsequent downfall of Atlantis (for which there was now plenty of factual evidence available, interestingly kept under wraps for most of the time) or not, the examples were there as plain as is possible to demonstrate, as to what happens when mankind starts to believe that it is separate from the universe.

The results in Atlantis were catastrophic, and the human race was heading for the same end once again. The catastrophe would not end with Planet Earth, but would be careered around the galaxy, bringing discord and disruption to all other civilisations within this universe, and other dimensions. Louise understood that as every choice a person makes within their soul incarnation spins off to create a parallel dimension, so does it affect every dimension in which they are incarnated. Every choice in this life quite literally affects all the past and future lives of an individual. Quantum physics proved this. The behaviour of photons of light, of collections of atoms when propelled through a zero-point energy field, demonstrated that the behaviour of life within this energy field produced more than one path, more than one direction each time it passed through. This had presented quite a conundrum for these scientists who had initially thought that the atom was making random choices each time. It was not until they extended their experiments to capture the movement of the particles in every direction possible, that they finally understood that so many paths were being taken simultaneously, always producing the same end result. Parallel realities!

With all the energy invested on this planet by scientists in the 21st century, together with the wisdom of many renowned and unrecognised people, old souls, living upon Planet Earth, to try and help to redress the balance of harmony, there was the knowledge and ability to dramatically change the future, and to finally bring about the dream of living in complete peace and harmony upon the earth and within all of the universe. When all the barriers and divisions came down upon earth, only then could the planetary and dimensional divides come down, bringing about a state of complete universal harmony.

Louise knew that in order for everything to be in harmony, mankind had to first accept that we are all part of the same energy source, the universe, and not separate from each other or from the universe in any way. Secondly, there had to be an understanding that for all to be in harmony, there has to be a perfect balance of the female and male energies in all things. This intrinsic balance was evident all around, in nature and in the elements. Sacred Geometry, the study of sound and structure being in perfect balance throughout the essence of life, was evidence of nature's balance. When the land, the people and the buildings could be in complete harmony energetically, so could life. Sound and structure, she knew, formed the very essence of everything that was life. It was interesting that feeling was the language of the soul, and music the language of feeling. She knew there were already plenty of examples of that truth in existence. It was essential now that, instead of being hidden away, the discovery of new things, so fundamentally important to mankind now, which relied upon the balance of female and male properties to reproduce in abundance, were made obvious to the peoples of the world.

A good example of this was energy. Louise had been studying ways to produce the completely clean and free energy that would be the basis of a number of the fundamental changes that she was writing about, crystal energy being the closest she had been able to determine. She knew that crystals had been used in Atlantis for almost all of its energy supplies, including for travel. It had been supported by a form of completely clean electromagnetic energy, which had been traversed across ley lines, and used for many things. She had recently discovered in a newspaper article, a company in Dublin who claimed to have found a source of completely clean, free, electromagnetic energy. What drew her to the newspaper article was the claim by the Chief Executive that this energy source was abundant, dependent only upon the existence of its component parts, and would therefore radically challenge the way we power the universe. Electro was male energy and magnetic was female energy. If produced as a completely clean energy source, it would be wholly contributive to the harmony of the universe.

The challenge, as was the challenge for many of these discoveries, was to create a group-consciousness of such proportions to be able to embrace an energy source that was free, clean and abundant. This would be at complete odds with the economics of the energy companies with their vast profits, and with the governments that supported them, as it could potentially render these companies redundant, presenting their governments with a substantial loss of income. It was vital therefore that humanity as a whole could perceive this in its true state, and not doctored by the institutions that stood to lose by such discoveries.

This was a very good example of why the group-consciousness of mankind needed to embrace the radical changes to the basis of life that Louise was directed through her book to put forward, and why a clear channel of communication needed to be put in place to enable this to happen. When she considered this, her heart became alive at its very core, for she knew beyond doubt that she would be instrumental in bringing to the fore a completely new way of presenting media, news, of expressing the inspirational truth in all things. She would set up, as part of the foundation she was to found, an entirely new way of bringing one's expression of the truth to the entire population of the world. This would be in the form of a media-publishing company. She knew now who many of the key people to be involved in this would be, and that the company would be combined with a groundbreaking structure to promote the notion that science was providing inextricable evidence right now, for the universal truth.

The vibrational energies being sent to earth were rapidly increasing. There was plenty of scientific proof of this around the planet now, proof collected and demonstrated through the use of tools such as Random Event Generators. This increase in energy vibration was the universe intent on enabling the consciousness of mankind to start to comprehend that we are all part of one energy source, and that we must therefore desire to change collectively. Planet Earth was literally becoming lighter, along with all of its inhabitants. This was a turning point for humankind. Louise had read this in many different ways. Planet Earth was starting its course for home, back to source, back to the light. There were 383 planets right now on an in-breath back to their core. Planet Earth was the jewel in the universe's crown,

the only one of these 383 that took with it a consciousness of its own.

Louise knew now, beyond all doubt, that the influential people that needed to come forward to help her
with her book were those who, like her, were prepared
at this time, the turn of the times, to speak and live
their truth. While she knew that by writing this book
she was bringing these changes to the world's attention,
she also understood that she was a facilitator, collecting
together all of the people the universe intended, at the
time the universe intended, to enable these changes to
occur. This was indeed divine timing.

The enormity of understanding coursed through her
senses as she considered that, with these few precious
hours left, it was time to perform a self-healing. It was
time to honour the bringing to a close of a quite remarkable awakening in her journey, her quest for all that is,
for the meaning of life. Louise prepared the room and
lit the candles. The self-healings, together with the unified chakra balancing, had been her daily sustenance,
always providing key guidance and messages. Since
returning from Rome, the ascended masters had been
even more omnipotent within the healing. She knew
that as 2006 drew to a close, with all the strong energies
of receiving indicated for 2007, that this would indeed
be a significant night for her.

Chapter 9

As Louise sat and started to take in the ambience, the candlelight, the soft Buddhist chants, she overwhelmingly knew that this healing was not to be for her, but for Ben. She called to the masters and angels for guidance, for this had been her sacred time, her promise to herself, her final peace before the beginning of the festivities to see in the New Year, and all the promise it held for her. She asked for reassurance three times, and every time the answer was crystal clear, this was to be an absent healing, for Ben.

Louise began by envisaging him on a bench in the park, but this swiftly moved, on His request, to a large, dark room. They were in a circle of candles, He sitting with his back to her, she standing. As the healing commenced, a circle of light grew around them, forming a wall of light and shrouding them within it. The ceiling, the walls and the floor fell away, leaving them suspended in space within the circle of light. She explained to Him that she was healing Him multidimensionally across all of his existences in every reality, allowing Him to merge his parallel realities back to a single one. She told Him that He had started walking through different dimensions to her at night, during her self-healings, pulling back the veil of each, walking closer and closer towards her. She had seen Him do this, shrouded by light as He walked forward. While He listened intently, the masters and angels told her to ask Him to stand, and then to lay Him on the stone altar that had appeared in the middle of the circle. She did this and He walked to the altar and lay down. She started to perform a chakra balance, which turned into a unified chakra balance, teaching Him to breathe in the light and unify all his chakras in one unified breath of light, something she had been doing avidly since embarking upon her path of lightbody surgery.

When she had finished the chakra balancing, the masters and angels asked her to take Him by the hand and bring Him to the crystal pyramid to see the very same angels she had visited when receiving her gifts of attunement. He stood, took her hand, and they flew through time and space, through the tunnels of light, the Void, and eventually to the top of the pyramid. As they flew to the ground together, He was asked to step forward. He did so, and knelt before the three great angels. She, still sitting in the physical in her healing position, asked for reassurance that this was really happening to him, although she knew it to be true. She felt, in the physical, the overwhelmingly reassuring presence of all the angels she could see in front of her in that pyramid. It made her weep. They looked upon Him, gently touching His head, imploring Him to come back to the light. They asked her to take Him back now, and as He stood to face her, she saw that He too was weeping. She took His hand and, just before leaving the pyramid to travel back through all dimensions to the altar, Archangel Raphael came to Him. He placed a hand on Ben's forehead and simply said, 'Come back to the light now, it is your time.'

Returning to the altar, Louise stood behind Him while He sat on the chair. She asked for any final healing to be given. He turned to look at her as more energy surged through her. He had tears streaming down his face, as did she. She could not hold back any longer, for she knew now that this healing was a gift granted to enable her to tell Him her truth through all lives, all dimensions, here now, when it mattered so much. She told Him that He could feel her, feel her love which spanned all time, that He had asked her in another lifetime to find a way to make Him take her face in his hands so that He may look upon her soul and know her once more. She confessed that she did not know how to do this. She still could not quite understand whether this Ben was her sacred love, although he looked so like Him. His very essence felt so familiar, and here she was being guided to perform healings for him once more. He must come back to the light, remember her and come to her. The tears were truly flowing, rendering her unable to utter anything in the physical. As He looked at her, she knew in his soul that at that moment there was some recollection. He took her face and lovingly told her that He would come back to her now.

Drawing the healing to a close, with all her soul Louise prayed for Archangel Michael to ground this healing into Him so that He may indeed come back to the light, and back to her now. She was convinced in that very moment, that now was the time for her to recognise the full significance of this union, of its origins in Atlantis, of the work she was carrying out in Atlantis, and its relevance to her relationship with this man. Many people had discussed the theoretical reasons for the fall of Atlantis, she however had been slowly but surely coming to a different realisation, one she felt ill-informed to substantiate right now.

* * *

That evening Louise headed off to a friend's house with her children in tow, to see in the New Year in quiet celebration. As the clock chimed midnight, the expectancy of all to come infused her being. After the festivities were over, she smiled with an absolute sense of conviction of all that was soon to come to pass. The weather had been atrocious when they arrived but, as they left the house, stepping out into the beauty of the calm, pitch-dark night, a whole host of birds were singing in chorus, as if in honour of her path. She climbed into the car and, it seemed, the universe was determined to ensure she had received the message loud and clear, for there on the dashboard were the numbers 444, 333 and 111.

New Year's Day was spent in laughter and fun with Floe, and when Louise climbed into bed, tired but rejuvenated with the thought that here she was in 2007, she put on a new Tibetan CD to commence a healing for herself. She had started to understand that there must be a deep connection at soul level with this man, Ben. She still could not quite understand, however, if he truly was this sacred partner or somebody who so resembled Him. There was no doubt that, from the very first moment that his energy had drawn her to him, there was an undeniable connection between them. Now here she was, being guided to heal him across all dimensions, all realities and to what avail? Surely it was he who had uncovered the deep-set love within her as she pieced together their past life connections. Or was it simply that he reminded her so much of another man, the other man? And yet, how could that be? His energy had called her, and surely that meant that his higher self, his soul, was calling her to a relationship of some kind with him, with his physical body. She was utterly confused.

As she started the multidimensional healing for herself, she found herself lying on a large stone altar in the dark of space, with one very large altar candle at her feet. As soon as the healing commenced she felt an enormous shunt of her bed in the physical, as if it had been shaken. She opened her eyes briefly, but nothing was there. She asked Archangel Michael for protection and he replied, 'I already am protecting you, don't worry.' She instantaneously felt the masters around her head and shoulders, but nowhere else. It was completely dark, with the exception of the light being thrown in streams from that one candle, and, as she looked towards her feet, she saw Ben walk forward from behind the light, dressed in a long white robe. He walked towards her, stood and looked at her. She asked Jesus why Ben had come to her. But He didn't answer. She asked Him again and, when He didn't answer for the second time, turned to ask Ben. 'I've come to heal you. I've come to love you,' He replied. He walked closer, still looking down at her. Tears fell silently down her face now. 'But you haven't contacted me in the physical,' she declared. He completely ignored this, and a knowing seemed to pass between them, as if the very fact that there had been no true exchange within the physical was entirely irrelevant to the reality they were to experience now. For what truly was reality? Suddenly Louise was aware that she was completely naked, lying quite still on the altar. As she lay there, completely comfortable with her nakedness, not feeling exposed in any manner, she understood that this had happened for Him. 'Why have you asked for me to be naked?' she implored. 'So that I may look upon your beauty,' He replied as He stood for what seemed an eternity just watching her. Then He dropped his robe and lay down beside her on the altar. He held her in his arms and it was as if they started to merge. She was so full of love it was almost unbearable. She looked at Him and understood that this soul lying with her now was without doubt her sacred partner, and the love of the ages flooded her being. She was totally engulfed in all that was their union. She could barely whisper her words for Him, 'Do you know how much I love you?' He held her and replied, 'Yes, as much as the magnificence of the entire universe, as much as I ever have loved, and ever will love you.' The lights in the entire house quite suddenly blacked out in the physical world. It was so shocking that Louise momentarily opened her eyes, still deeply in the multidimensional, feeling him lying with her on the altar. She was aware of both Archangel Michael and Archangel Azrael, who reassured her that they had been protecting them both throughout. She lay with Him that way for some time, until the lights quite suddenly came back on in the house. Ben then got up, robed them both, and slowly walked away. She prayed with all her soul for understanding, for what she had just experienced was beyond description. She stood and glanced in the mirror, and saw that she was surrounded by an emerald-green light all the way up to her crown, and that a golden light emanated from around her crown.

Louise hardly slept that night, as she was trying to come to terms with the significance of what was happening to her. She was beyond words and felt as though she did not know which way to turn, or what to do. The next day she spoke to Floe. Her dear friend explained the significance of what she was beginning to encounter. 'Within Atlantis,' she explained, 'the merging of the two bodies was a significant part of the extraordinary union of sacred partners. This was quite literally the coming together of two people on every level, the spiritual and the physical. This form of union was what was always intended by the universe to be utter expression of divine love. Allow Him to come to you now, to love you, and just be. Allow all to unfold within your union as it is to unfold. You are both experiencing the recall of your union and the magnificent beginning of coming together once more. This is your twin soul, the very first split of your essence, and in the coming back together, you will bring back divine love to this reality, and harmony to you both. Do not place attachment to the physical man you have encountered, know only that this man who comes to you now is, beyond all doubt, your sacred partner, your love, and returns to you to stand by you now as he always promised that he would.'

Every night now He came to their healing. Constantly she was being urged to heal their relationship across all realities and all dimensions. Although she didn't understand where this could be leading in the physical, she followed her instructions implicitly, as she was being urged. Always the masters and angels held her, held him, cherishing their togetherness. Every day she longed for nightfall, for the moment of their union, their closeness. As her lightbody sessions brought her own soul closer to her, so her connection with all within the universe was growing at a remarkable rate. In parallel, the healing was becoming so intense, so profound, that she yearned for these times of knowledge, of understanding and of love.

* * *

Two weeks had passed since the healings had become so intense, and when Louise began a new healing, a healing for them both across all dimensions, she had no idea that this would bring her the vision of the true purpose of her task.

Standing within a circle of bright altar candles, in the darkness of space, surrounded by beautiful beings of light, He looked intensely upon her face. She turned from Him and started walking up several stone steps towards a majestic podium. At the top she lay on a large stone altar, her clothes disappearing, to be replaced with a long white robe, which fell gracefully over the edges of the altar. He followed, his clothing changing, so that He was also wearing a robe by the time He reached the altar. He sat next to her and slowly enveloped her within Him as they sat together, their robes falling away. He pulled her hair towards him, his hand gently caressing the back of her head, and they held each other tightly as if the holding expressed their togetherness for all time, for all eternity, the love of all the ages entwined. The light of their love, their togetherness was so pure. After some time they stood, walked back down the stone steps, hand in hand and, as they reached the bottom, turned to face one another once more, clothed as before.

When the healing finished and Louise lay in bed contemplating all that had taken place, the incredible intensity of their love, and how and when it could possibly manifest itself in this reality, a vision took hold of her. As this vision unfolded in front of her eyes, she could not quite believe what she was seeing. The vision became complete and she opened her eyes, tears coursing down her face as the realisation sank in that she had just witnessed the events which were to unfold and conclude the book she was writing, the story of humanity's return to consciousness, the story of the sacred love of these two. It took some time before she was able to sleep, and when sleep did finally come, it was sporadic.

The next day she received a lightbody activation session in which Floe had quite unexpectedly been directed to sing the language of light to her, through her crown. As she did so, both girls were moved to tears, for this, they both recognised, was the very same chant she had sung in Atlantis at that sacred union ceremony. This marked a turning point for them both, as, for her friend, it was the resumption of an ancient, rare and beautiful practice to now finally become part of her soul's manifestation here. For Louise it marked the beginning of her transcription of knowledge from her inner labyrinth.

The very next morning saw her wake with her vision full of script and symbols. She had no idea what they were or what they meant but, as she was guided to do, she started to write them down in a book for safekeeping. She was told by the masters not to attempt to decipher them for now, just to keep them safe, and all would become clear as more information was given to her.

And it was.

Chapter 10

It was a beautiful sunny day and, after so many days being cooped up in the house, Louise rejoiced at being able to return to the castle gardens, to feel the elements, to rejoice in nature, and to receive the inspiration she always felt when writing there. While she waited to pay for her lunch, which she would take up to the gardens with her, she pondered for a brief moment on how it had been so long since she had seen Ben now, since she had given him the CD and note, and yet he came to her every night. Whenever she started to question why he was coming to her at night and yet not during the day, her thoughts were always drawn back to that very first time she had seen him, when his soul had called to her in this supermarket. That energy connection had been so strong, he had called to her so clearly, and yet still nothing had come of it. She knew deep within her soul that this was the essence, the beauty, the magnificence of divine timing, and trusted implicitly that things would unfold as they should, as so many things were unfolding for her now.

On her way up to the castle gardens, considering all of this as she walked, she turned and unexpectedly found herself face-to-face with a friend of his who she had seen Ben with on a number of previous occasions.

As a look of recognition crossed his face, Louise's intuition told her to speak to him. She knew so well by now to follow her soul's message that the words were out of her mouth without a moment's thought. 'You are Ben's friend,' she said. He agreed and asked how she knew Ben, and she explained that she had spoken to him a few times, that she was writing a book and had talked to Ben believing he could help her with it. He smiled and chatted a while as they strolled up through the gardens. He smiled, said that he would tell Ben she'd said 'Hi,' and walked away to work.

Louise sat in the gardens and, again, the elements danced and sung around her, providing deep knowing and inspiration for her writing. In these quiet moments her mind was filled with a knowing, an understanding, a dialogue with the universe. She was now becoming so used to having these dialogues with the divine. It was beauty indeed, for her writing was utterly inspired by the intensity of the exchanges between them. As she sat studying the script which had been channelled through her consciousness all those weeks ago, she called upon her ever-increasing understanding of the elements, and the sacred structure held within these elements. She had been studying Sacred Geometry and was determined to understand whether there were any synergies within the structure and shapes of her script, and the geometric shapes within her study book. She knew that somehow her script was embodying elements of the structure of these geometric forms and was determined to understand which elements were being embodied, in order to further understand the purpose of the script itself. Time soon passed, and Louise headed back down the hill towards work.

The following day she dropped her children at school and drove to see a clairvoyant channel called Diana, whose pamphlet she had picked up at a meeting, and who had been highly recommended to her by three different sources. Diana had been clairvoyant since childhood, possessed goddess and void skills, crystal skills, Gaiadon heart keys and ascension mystery school teachings, but it was her Atlantis Angelise knowledge and teachings that drew Louise to her. For Louise knew that the success of her soul's purpose in this incarnation relied heavily upon the wisdom she carried with her from Atlantis, her knowledge of the secrets that had been kept for so long, her deep connection to those energies, and her sacred union from that lifetime, bound across time and space. She was sure that as well as channelling messages from the universe, which were appropriate for her now, Diana would become instrumental in giving her the keys to unlock the knowledge and secrets within.

When she had spoken to Diana on the telephone the previous week to make the appointment, she knew this to be true. She was not, however, prepared for the extent of the information she was to have imparted to her on this occasion. Diana was an exquisite, articulate and well-educated lady with a truly charming manner about her. As Louise sat, absorbed by the information and messages flowing through her, she was at a loss for words. She did not recognise herself in the person Diana and the universe were referring to, and yet, somehow, it all rang so true. The universe knew what lay within Louise, knew of her ancestry, of her lineage, of her preparation for this, her soul's journey. It was because of all these things that the universe had decided that it was quite befitting for her to understand more now. She would not be overwhelmed by what lay ahead of her. All that she needed to enable her to complete her purpose was within her. The keys and codes she would use to release this knowledge from within her inner labyrinth of knowledge, were to be gradually released now. And yet still she was only to know what was appropriate at this juncture.

Her twin soul was to play a key role in her future, and this soul, with whom she was now reforming such a strong bond within the ether was indeed her sacred partner, her twin soul. The pioneers she would rely upon to help her in her quest would come forward and find her, she was told. She would not need to seek them out, they would find her through her book, and through the work she was about to carry out. It was important that she trust in the universal plan, and understand that she was truly blessed, as would be all those who sought to join her. She would have to trust at all times in the perfection of order and timing, for universal timing and order would not always be as she expected.

Making her way home, Louise understood that she was indeed truly blessed, for as she contemplated the

way so many things within her book were becoming
reality right now, there could be no other explanation.

* * *

It was her birthday, and Louise knew somehow that
this would be a day on which she would receive treasure and riches from the universe. The treasure of the
knowledge of life, of the essence of love, was all she
truly desired on this or any other day.

Led by her beautiful eldest son, who endeavoured
as always to ensure that the others followed suit, her
children brought cards and presents to her in her
bed. Basking in their shining light of love and compassion, Louise knew that this day would indeed be
special. For as she had awoken at 5:55 a.m., the divine
had recommenced conversations with her once more.
As the days passed by, the longer the dialogues
became, the thirstier she was to continue them. All
else paled by comparison with the illumination of
these moments.

When she thought back to the many times over the
years that she had tried to speak with the universe in
this way, how she had prayed and thought that she had
heard the voice of God, she realised that she had never
truly heard the universe at all. The direct communication she was having now, filled her with the most astonishing knowing, and the most wonderful sense of being
and of love. The answers, the wisdom she was receiving, the questions she was able to ask, were beyond the

boundaries of any wisdom available within humanity as she knew it. The wondrous beauty, the clarity and the authenticity of the answers she received, were like the sunlight breaking through the dawn. It was as if all time stood still while the simplest, and yet most profound, knowledge flowed through her and enabled her to finally understand some of the greatest mysteries of the universe.

She knew that today of all days, these answers were not for the book she was writing now, but should be treasured and stored for a time when she was to be directed to reveal them. As she wrote, she was reminded that there was no need to believe that she would not remember the information that she was receiving, for she would of course be reminded of all these details in line with divine timing. These days were for her to fully understand and appreciate her path, her soul's choice and the reasons for her astonishing knowledge, which appeared to have been borne within her writing.

Julie, called early in the morning, as she always did, to ensure that all was well, to send her love, and to gently remind Louise to be kind to herself. Louise was full of a deep desire to be with Cherry by the time she arrived to receive her reiki, and as they started their all-so-familiar dialogue, marvelling at the revelations now occurring at such a pace, they both felt the intensity of the divine love that surrounded them. It was so appropriate, Louise knew, that she be here with Cherry today, for she had always felt, from the very first moment their energies had connected, so close to her, so much a part of her heavenly family.

From the moment Louise lay down and started to receive the reiki, she felt the familiar knowing of Jesus at her head, and Mary Magdalene at her feet. This filled her with an overwhelming love. This time, however, was the first time that she had seen Ben come to her here, for here He was at her side, holding her hand. He remained there until the healing was finished. As she sat up, she noticed the emotion, the tears within Cherry's eyes as she explained the deep shifts that had taken place. She had seen the Magdalene flame infuse seven layers of energy within Louise, and all the while she had been loved and shrouded by Jesus. Louise knew this to be true, as she had felt the force of that love rise within her, bringing with it a complete sense of protection and of inspiration.

* * *

That evening, as Louise drove home from an evening celebrating with friends, she knew within her heart that she would always feel the deep bond of unconditional love, of longing, of grief, and of repletion between Jesus and Mary Magdalene. With all her soul she wanted the world to finally understand the beauty and the depth of the love that passed between them, of their path, of the choice of Mary Magdalene to support this man, of their deep and sacred bond across all time, and of the truth of their existence. As she spoke to the universe, pledging to the universe with a steely will that she would bring this knowledge to the world now, and no longer allow this beauty to be swept aside, a stunning and blinding white light streaked across the sky in front of her. It broke through the dark of night and filled the sky as if to declare to all that this indeed would come to pass. This filled Louise with so much love and wonder and deep determination, and it was with these feelings that she finally fell into her slumber that night.

The very next day, as the weather drew in, bringing bitterly cold winds, she craved the solitude of the castle gardens once more. She wrapped up warmly and walked up towards the gardens, feeling so moved by the events of the week, and she had a deep knowing that, once more, the universe was about to reveal something through her, something quite profound. She sat on the bench, eating her food with difficulty because she was shaking with the intensity of the energy coursing through her. She was told by the universe to pick up her pen and start writing. She felt exhilarated with the anticipation of what was to come, for at that precise moment, as the divine was lovingly and urgently imploring her to commence, she knew beyond doubt that this was a message for her meeting she was to have the following week with the chief executive of an energy company in Dublin. She had spoken to this man the day before her birthday, and when he had heard about what she was writing about, he had told her to come and see him. The message that she was now receiving filled her with absolute knowing, a total conviction that these changes were indeed to occur, on a planetary scale, very soon.

* * *

Louise wrote:

> *This book will rock the foundations of humanity's beliefs. Finally the world will be brought to an understanding of who and what they are, of their oneness, of the essential nature and essence of the universe, of its component parts, and of its harmony and balance. They will understand that only in harmony and balance can humanity hope to exist. Harmony and balance is, in essence, the absolute balance of feminine and masculine and, after millennia of male-dominated ethics and morals, there are those upon this planet prepared to step forward and declare their allegiance to harmony, to declare their allegiance to the universe.*

> *These people, once united, will form a force so formidable on this planet, that society as you know it will indeed be set upon its head. Governments will rock, and any institution or corporation operating on any basis that is not in harmony with universal good WILL FALL. The knowledge these people will bring from eons of lifetimes, from their soul, is the very essence of change that will propel these radical changes forward.*

> *Because these changes have the complete and best interests of the universe and planetary consciousness at heart, the creator will co-create with these people, these pioneers, at an alarming rate, in order to manifest these changes upon earth. The universe will mobilise all peoples, places and events, to support these radical changes to once again bring harmony and heaven to earth.*

Reading back these words she had written, and taking in the full force of the intent empowered through these words, Louise basked in the glory of the universe. She sat with the universe for some time in deep dialogue, marvelling at the wonders ahead. She understood these words to be truly a gauntlet, laid down for all who read and understood their intent. She knew beyond doubt that those people, the pioneers to come forward to her through her book, would truly be those of which the universe had spoken, people she now believed to have been as one in Atlantis. She felt enthralled, exhilarated and blessed beyond measure at the thought of the wonder of working with these people.

Chapter 11

It was with a weary heart at the prospect of her husband returning today to reside under the same roof once more, that Louise knew she could do this no longer. She had waited so patiently for their house to sell, to allow him this time to come to terms with the inevitable parting, and to help him to understand how much she still cared, and how his children always were and always would be so close to him. But this last week had shown her how much she longed for her space. It had shown her how inspired she was able to be when within her space, able to be who she was meant to be. Not for one moment did she hold animosity of any sort towards her husband, quite the contrary, but she had given him enough time now to come to a sense of acceptance and they had, by holding that intention so firmly, come to a sense of calm. Now, having had this last week's space and quiet, truly a gift from the universe in the light of what she had learnt and the events that had taken place, she understood that this space, this separation was essential for her to be able to complete her work. And this work was needed right now, with not a moment to waste.

She also knew that a sense of true calm had settled in the house over this period, in which the children had truly relaxed, for, although consciously they still had not been told, they all knew intuitively what was ahead. The fear of the situation to come was far worse than the reality, which she knew would be fully and abundantly supported by the universe. Her eldest son was to change schools later that year and, with the long summer holidays ahead, a time of change in itself, she knew that he would need a period of calm and settled transition ahead of him, to know that all was well and calm, and that love was still abundant.

Sitting amid the wind and the trees, these thoughts weighing heavily upon her, the divine spoke to her in a reassuring manner, and she realised that her body ached, for the emotion of this last week had been quite extraordinary. The space which had given birth to her ability to start to commune with, to have these wonderful dialogues with the divine, had also brought a far closer bond to her heavenly family, through the knowledge of who and what she was. She was no longer a single-dimensional being. She was now living every moment in multiple dimensions.

She drove into the countryside and parked her car beneath a canopy of dark-wooded trees. She craved one last opportunity to be truly alone and, as she sat listening to her music, her soul cried out to her, imploring her to complete a self-healing. The moment she started this healing for herself alone, something she had not done since before the New Year, she was told that the time had come for all ties to her husband to be lovingly severed. As the masters spoke the words of the vow breaks, she slowly repeated them and, as she did so, it was as if a lightness entered her, and all her deep aching disappeared.

As she left that place and drove home, she understood that she was finally ready, ready for all that lay ahead of her. She was restored. A joy, a rapturous delight, filled her every essence. She felt anointed by the universe with love, and inspiration was once again her friend. As she laughed and joked with the divine and they animatedly discussed their purpose, the wonder of everything that lay ahead unfolded in front of her eyes in exquisite detail. She felt the simple and yet profound wonder of what was now undoubtedly going to happen. And here she was. So honoured, so delighted, and so filled with love and gratitude to be at the centre of this wondrous task, co-creating with the universe.

As they delighted together, she told the divine that they were partners now and, as such, they must treat one another so, respecting each other's comments and wishes. It was a serious bond that required a serious pledge, she had said. They must make this pledge to one another across all time and space, all realities, and the universe would hold their pledge true. And their pledge was that they would indeed remain partners to co-create the wondrous reality laid forth in the story of her book and beyond. This was a sacred pledge, they reminded each other, as sacred as any ever taken, and in that knowledge they delighted and talked at pace about the beauty and wonder of the plan ahead.

As she described the ethics of the foundation to be established, that those who dedicated themselves and worked within the foundation would be rewarded with the abundance and riches of heaven for their love and impassioned drive to renew this universe, the divine most certainly agreed. For the abundance of heaven was far greater than any material riches, although the divine assured her at her prompting that no one person would be left wanting, all would have their fundamental material needs met. It was with this excitement and delight that they continued to talk well into the night until, the hours having slipped silently past, Louise noticed that she was once again under that same roof without her own space. She knew now, beyond all doubt, that this would no longer be her life. She needed only to exercise one last tiny period of patience while the universe made manifest her intentions.

Standing at her bedroom window, looking out into the dark of the night that lay ahead, she unwittingly focussed all her attention upon the pioneers that were to materialise now. It was as if she had captured every essence of energy emanating from her dialogue with the divine, from the love and delight they shared, into a single thread of consciousness, a direct message she now channelled to each and every pioneer. And as she felt the beauty of the dark night fill her, and spoke with all her soul to these pioneers, laying down the gauntlet to join her side and be in co-creation of this wondrous vision with her and the universe, she knew that they had heard and would now respond.

* * *

Lying in bed as instructed, Louise commenced a healing for her and Ben. As He walked to her, looked upon her, her radiance reflected in his face, she knew that He finally now saw her for who she truly was. As she spoke, with grace and ease, the words flowed eloquently. No pain was within her now, only the pure divine love and joy of her sense of being, for she was supported by all that was love. She had the most wonderful heavenly family holding her, and she felt the strength of the universe coursing within her, filling her every breath, dancing within her soul. Still her love for Him was as constant and bright as it had always been. But this night she laid down their gauntlet too, for now she knew that every person by her side, including this wonderful man she loved so deeply, would hold within their heart what she held and saw within hers.

Louise told him that their soul must choose, desire, yearn for, and be absolutely intent upon achieving, that which she and the universe had set before them. If Ben was truly her twin soul, truly who she believed Him to be, then He would embrace this with joy, and would stand with her in full expectation, delight and determination to achieve their soul's purpose. He smiled at her in the way that she so loved, took her hand, and they stood before the divine. It was his joy to pledge his oath before the universe and to become part of this wondrous journey and team. He picked her up and in joy they danced and danced and laughed and laughed, and all of the universe danced and laughed with them.

As this healing finished and Louise lay in wonder and joy at what she had just experienced, at the empowering of all of these wonderful people, she fell into a deep and blissful sleep. She had no idea if the man named Ben she continually met in town was this man, this soul who came to her now, but of one thing she was so sure. This soul was without doubt her love across the ages, her twin soul, and she knew that the universe would bring Him to her in perfect timing.

* * *

On waking the next morning, joy instantaneously flooded Louise's every sense. By nightfall, as she sat and wrote at the computer, she marvelled at yet more revelations, at her knowing of all who had been with her etherically all day, and at the shock of understanding that Ben was now starting to talk to her in her waking moments as well. Earlier that day she had been in the bathroom, laughing with Archangel Azrael, who had commented on how he had done a pretty good job transforming her body lately. She had asked if he could finally get rid of her stretch marks, and when he had asked why, she had simply replied that although she loved to see herself so radiant, it was not for her but for Ben that she wished to look beautiful. And then she heard Ben, as clearly as she heard the divine: 'You are beautiful,' He had said, and so had begun a tiny, but significant, dialogue together, where she had felt a sense of his being with her, holding her hand, and a deep sense of Namasté as she felt his energy caress the tip of her nose.

But as she sat at her computer that evening and wrote, weary from a long day and all the physical emotion brought on by the joy of more revelations, the pathos in what she was writing started to take hold of her. She thought of the separation and divorce ahead, of her children's future, and she started to falter. But the divine kept talking, never for one moment stopping. The divine caressed her with words and love and absolute reassurance that to live in love was the only way to live upon this earth, within this universe. Divine love was the bliss of life, the very essence of existence. And her children would indeed live in a love so abundant that she couldn't quite imagine yet. She always had been, and always would be, the mother that they needed, for what more could a child need than pure, abundant love?

The divine reminded her of how she was writing within her book about removing the very fear from humanity which prevented them from living in an enlightened state of love. And it would be by achieving this state of heightened bliss, by her example of how to tread where many others did not, to live her every moment in complete love of the universe and all around, which would demonstrate that love always would abound within her family. Her husband would find peace. He would come to understand how much their relationship had, and always would, mean to her. With these words still echoing in her head, she fell deeply and instantaneously to sleep.

Chapter 12

'Absolute knowing is what made Jesus turn water into wine, feed 5,000 with but a few loaves of bread, walk on water.' These were the words the universe was speaking to her as she opened her eyes the next morning.

'He did not believe He was doing this, He truly knew He was. It is this absolute knowing that enabled him to co-create with me, to manifest these wonderful things upon the earth. And this, child, is why we will do the same, for you already know this to be true, as it has already begun to happen for you and me. This message is key, for in order to change this planet, this is what it will take. It will not take many to ensure these changes happen, but a few within the grand scheme of things, and you and I will mobilise these people from now. You have read how few people it will take.'

And at that moment, when the divine spoke of the conviction that such a small number of people would be required to fulfil the task ahead, that Louise realised the significance of a discussion she had had with Julie only the day before, after she had been reading a book called *Power Vs. Force*. Little more than 8,000 people would be required to reach a level of living entirely and constantly in a state of love, to counteract the consciousness of the entire world's population of over 6 billion people. This would be enough to change all of humanity's consciousness.

Louise and Julie had booked themselves places at the world's largest ever intention experiment workshop, to be held that March in London by a lady called Lynne McTaggart, and the eminent scientists with whom she worked. Louise had been wondering about the combined power of knowing with the ability to clearly define and set in place intention, and it dawned upon her that her experiences were all falling so wonderfully into place within the plan which had been set in motion between the divine and her soul from the very outset of time. She had been told for so long now that March would be the month when she would finally be who she was truly meant to be. Now, she understood that it had been no mistake that her intuition had been telling her for some time now to contact Lynne McTaggart. It must be in order for the scientific world to understand, and validate her book.

Louise now knew that Lynne McTaggart would surely know and understand the power of what she was writing about. The people that would be attending the conference (and those all around the world who couldn't get to London and would be taking part in the intention experiment via the Internet), would be there because they truly believed they could alter reality through their intention. These were the very people who would believe in the reality, who would will and know the reality within her book to be true. Once these intention experiments, instigated by Lynne McTaggart's group, had been successfully achieved on such a scale, who of all those people attending the conference and taking part in the experiment online, who had created the end results, would say 'that can't be done again'? And the answer was simply and profoundly this. NO ONE. When the magnitude of this revelation took hold of her, of knowing that this story within her book was, and always had been, intended to be a huge step towards humanity's elevated consciousness, she could only sit quietly. And then she cried, tears of under-standing, tears of exhilaration and tears of love and, as she did so, she felt her great partner do so, too. For in her the mother/father God had found what they had always known her to be, their hope.

* * *

Every night now, Ben came to Louise. Each time the experience became more and more intense, as she felt his body in every way. And not only did He come to her at night, but also during her days. He talked to her con-stantly, held her, caressed her, laughed with her, and in every way honoured her. She was so utterly at a loss for words over all that was happening to her. If it were not for the many close friends who understood her entirely, she could quite easily have thought herself crazy. For so many of these friends, that which she was experiencing now was not a new notion.

She felt great delight when she was told that the time was soon approaching when the profound understanding would enter her consciousness, which would help her to understand more of the path she must follow with this man. The night before her trip to Dublin was one that marked a major shift in this relationship. In every sense He made love to her for many hours that night, and she, moved to a point of complete understanding of their divine and sacred connection, was left trembling with the overwhelming love coursing through her very essence. As the early morning came and she got herself out of bed, she knew that there would never be a time now when they would be apart. As she heard the delighted screams of the children downstairs, she walked to the window to see the cause of their delight. The sky was filled with beautiful, white winter snow, and she knew this to be a sign from the universe, as if the universe were sending confetti to mark the celebration of her sacred union once more.

Arriving at Dublin Airport that morning, as she stepped foot onto the Irish soil, the familiar sense of coming home took hold of her. The cab driver, quite delighted at hearing the story of why she was in Dublin that day, was determined to provide the history of the bar where she had met Adrian all those weeks ago. The Capital Lounge, he had explained, was owned by the very same family who owned Lilly Bardello's and Judge Roy Bean. The same family now owned a very famous bar, the Mont Claire, in New York. As they chatted animatedly, and he questioned her at length about the book she was writing, about her experiences, and assured her that he would pick her up again later that day, Louise noticed that all around her there were messages from the universe. Each car they followed was decked with the numbers 55555 and 111111. 555 she knew to be a sign of major changes occurring within a person's life, changes that would propel a person towards a life they truly deserved, and 111, she understood, was a sign of a huge energetic gateway opening, enabling a person's thoughts to be manifested into reality at extraordinary speed. As she hopped out of the taxi, she took the driver's card and promised to ring him again.

From the moment the chief executive of the energy company arrived, it was as if a long-lost friend had walked right in through the door. They had agreed that they would meet some weeks before when, in a telephone discussion, he understood that the book she was writing detailed the need for a clean, abundant and universally harmonious energy source. This energy source she had been looking for was something his company had produced and were in the process of having validated. As he sat listening to her talk, she explained that she did not need him to prove to her that his energy source was authentic in its claim to be pure, abundant, and dependent only upon its component parts being in place. She knew that this form of energy was an inherent part of the energy system used in Atlantean times, and that it had been the universe's intention to bring it back to the fore in line with divine timing. In fact, she had just recently completely and utterly refuted a paper by another company claiming to have discovered something similar. She had astounded herself with the irrefutable knowledge she had had at her fingertips. The issue these two discussed, was not the ability of the energy source to do just what this company was claiming, but just how to enable the people to have access to it. In employing some of the world's top scientists to validate this energy source, they were going to ensure that the world heard what was happening, and what exactly was available. In the distribution of its essence via Web technology, making it available to all industries to purchase and integrate into their own systems, in much the same way that Internet search engines brought the power of unlimited knowledge to the people, so the people would have the power to take charge of their situation.

When Louise read him the directive she had been dictated the week before, he was astounded. They sat for hours, forgoing all other meetings, and just talked about the incredible synchronicities becoming apparent. For people Louise had started to contact were the very same people that he had been in contact with, and was working with now in various ways and in several countries. Hours later, as they hugged and Louise left for the airport, she knew she had once again found a firm friend. She thought how wonderful it would be when they would be able to work together as part of this foundation, exploring new ways of bringing harmony and balance to the scientific explorations now taking place, and driving science forward hand-in-hand, with the understanding of the creation of consciousness, or rather creation from consciousness. When she arrived home that night, a blanket of snow awaited. She slipped straight into bed and, exhausted, but completely and utterly held and protected, fell into a deep sleep.

While she had been talking with the chief executive, one of the synchronicities they had discovered was a fringe scientist in Texas whom he had been asked to go and see. This scientist was an expert in Breakthrough Propulsion Physics, and the following day, Louise started to read an article about his research. He had been leading a team of fringe scientists, quantum physicists, who were interested in his energy source to determine its potential viability as an alternative energy source for use in space travel. This was zero-point energy. Large passenger airtravel companies who were now looking into space travel, were working with this scientist, and she knew at least one company-owner would be someone set to be a pioneer working with her in her foundation.

Once again Louise found it strange that she recalled all the information now flooding her consciousness, which agreed with and extended the current theories of evolutionary physics. As she read further into the article, she mused about the current obsession with limiting travel to the constraints of this universe. Everything was measured still in distance and speed. The Breakthrough Propulsion Physics Program (BPP), established by NASA in 1966 to research advanced forms of space transportation, was to focus on three objectives:

- Propulsion that required no propellant mass
- Propulsion that attained the maximum transit speeds physically possible
- Breakthrough methods of energy production to power such devices

The programme had been suspended when NASA deleted its budget in 2003. This was at a point when Jordan Maclay, the chief scientist for Quantum Fields LLC, was seeking more empirical evidence to flesh out exactly what this Vacuum energy stuff (zero-point energy or ZPE) really was, by completing precise measurements of attractive Casimir forces, and working to quantify repulsive forces.

There was no doubt that science was working towards an understanding of the nature of the consciousness of the universe through the understanding of the quantum, or vacuum field. This was determined to be the zero-point energy field. Scientists understood that the fractal nature of the universe was directly linked to the nature of the zero-point energy field. This mass of dark matter, which was evident in the fractal studies exploring how galaxies owed their existences to cold dark matter (CDM), determined that creation really is based upon a fractal and vacuum concept. Louise noted how simple the step was to convert this understanding to a place of knowing that, in fact, rather than the dark mass creating the existence of all life forms, that it was the very consciousness and existence of the life form itself which created the existence of the dark mass. The two were irrevocably linked, intertwined, bound to the creation of the other.

Reading on, she learnt that a Dr Hal Putoff, Director for the Institute of Advanced Studies, secured private funding to continue the BPP Program, and lead a team of scientists to further explore zero-point energy for space travel. Comparing ZPE to nuclear energy, he explained:

'It's ridiculous, but theoretically, there's enough ZPE in the volume of a coffee cup to more-than evaporate all the world's oceans. But that's if you could get all of it and you obviously can't. So when it comes to a practical amount of ZPE that can be extracted from the vacuum, you're still talking about maybe 10 to the power of 26 joules/cubic meters. The potential is practically limitless, way beyond what can be conceived. But until we learn what ZPE embodiment to use, and to what frequency we can effectively extract the energy, it's really hard to make a practical statement about how much you can actually use. So far the embodiments are pitifully small, but the potential is there.'

Louise continued to read about how that staggering potential had kept researchers pursuing a quantum physics, which some critics classify as near-science-fiction. Even Einstein's equations, although he did not advocate a theory that in any way pointed to a quantum vacuum, showed that an infinitesimal amount of mass could be converted into a tremendous amount of energy via nuclear reactions (an energy source discovered by the Atlanteans). Einstein had been yet another master who had sought to further the comprehension and consciousness of humanity to bring it closer to an understanding of the oneness of the universe, of the essence of life.

As she continued to read, Louise quite incredibly found herself refuting and then concurring with different aspects of the reams of information she began to digest and glean from articles and Web enquiries. It was as if a light switched on in her consciousness. She had such a deep knowing that the uncovering of this step of transference from the study of travel within this universe, to that of the multi-dimensions, was that which she was here to pursue, and which she had deep recollections of working upon. Within this lifetime she had never even vaguely been interested in science. In fact she laughed as she recalled how she had been literally forced to choose a science subject at school, preferring always arts and literature. And yet here she was, practically gagging with her desire to research and understand more and more, to somehow link it to the knowledge that she knew she held deep within. She did not know where this was leading, but she knew that to ask the universe to take her along this path of discovery was certainly what she desired.

She had, from the moment she had conceived the bones of the book that one evening, been writing the strangest scientific concepts as they appeared to her. She knew that, as she read more about evolutionary physics, the knowing within merged with the evidence being drawn forth from the scientific world, to present an intense understanding of the path ahead. She had begun the process of assimilating within her consciousness all that she knew to be the teachings of the great masters, the philosophers, the scientists and their undeniable understanding of the basis of life. The link between science and philosophy was poetic. In Atlantis, she had now begun to recall the oneness of the teachings and practices of the two. She remembered The Children of the Law of One, who in group meditation in Atlantis, left their bodies and entered into the realms of fourth-dimensional consciousness to achieve increased knowledge and understanding, and penetrated the darkness to access the wisdom of the universe. They used a stone, called The Tuaoi Stone, to help bridge the gap between inner and outer reality. Certain events were recorded within the Akashic Records, the pictorial memories of all events, actions and feelings that have occurred since the beginning of time.

'Oh to be able to stand upon the shores of that land once more,' Louise thought. Cosmologists and theoretical physicians and the science of now, were intensely preoccupied with the first few fractions-of-a-second of the newborn universe, when all its energy, they believed, became manifest, together with the fundamental particles and fundamental fields of nature, of Gaia. They called this The Superstring Theory, proposing the existence of a primal unified field in ten dimensions – nine of space and one of time. As the universe expanded and cooled, they explained that the symmetries of this one unified field were broken, and the known fields of physics separated one-by-one from the unified field. They believe that this happened at different speeds, giving rise to the quantum field, the electromagnetic field, and others. This scientific concept of the unified field eminent scientists such as Dr Rupert Sheldrake had compared to the cosmic soul. Philosopher Plotinus, in the third century AD, spoke of the cosmic soul thus: 'There is both soul and many souls. From the one soul proceed a multiplicity of souls.' Evolutionary physicists now declared, 'There is both the one field and the many fields. From the one field proceed a multiplicity of fields.' Both were describing the undeniable presence of divinity, of oneness, in its true sense, just as they had been taught in Atlantis, where the ability to use the unified field was the key to the state of being.

Chapter 13

L ouise found that her ability to focus upon the here and now was becoming challenged, as her thirst was to lock herself away so that she could retreat into a state of being, and uncover all the knowledge that was within as it merged with science and literature in its evolutionary state. As the days passed by, she knew beyond doubt that this was oneness, for Ben never left her. The feelings within her were beyond words, beyond description. His thoughts were within hers, hers within his, their love bound so tightly now. He held her, caressed her, honoured her love and her beauty at all times. They talked, laughed, teased, strategised and loved for every moment of the day and night.

Driving into town one day, she felt sure that she would see Him, and she began to talk to the masters, to Jesus. Even as she parked, she felt his love within her, rising once more, leaving her trembling and expectant. As she walked into the supermarket she was so sure that she would glance across to see Him in another queue, that they would, upon seeing one another, start to experience this incredible love, there and then. As she felt His love draw nearer and nearer, she felt it welling within her. And then she saw Him, for the merest second, the clearest image she had seen of Him since

He had been coming to her etherically. He was gone again and she felt a deep sense of hurt, of disappointment, and of betrayal. As she strode up to Castle Gardens, book and lunch in hand, snow falling around her, she longed for the solitude the gardens gave her, and for the inspiration of the elements infused within that sacred ground. She had felt the vibrations of energy within that very ground ever since, during one of her healings, she had sunk an etheric crystal deep below the base of the ground.

Sitting on a bench, contemplating the week's events, Louise knew that the world-at-large would think her crazy. For how could she, in this three-dimensional world, be so in love with an etheric being? But she knew, for the power of her soul was such, that this dimension was not reality, but merely a beautiful expression of energy in dense matter. That reality is and always would be the reality of the love of the soul, the love of the universe. She knew that Ben would come to her in physical form in divine timing, and she marvelled at the wonder of divine timing as she watched more and more of her book's story unfold in front of her eyes. As she thought about the way the very words within this book had started to become reality, projected in entirety into the physical manifestation of people, places and events, her heart was filled with the joy and yearning to bring about this wondrous journey. When she thought of the people she was talking to, of how she had stated in her book that these pioneers could only stand with her if they had within their heart what she had within hers, she delighted that this had proved to be entirely true. For all those she was meeting now were exactly like this.

However, she could not understand what more could she do to manifest this relationship into reality. Without warning, she began to slip gently into a sudden feeling of yearning for Him, desperate for Him to hold her in physical form, and love her. A deep sense of sadness, and completely irrational betrayal, overwhelmed her. It was at this very moment, when her heart felt as if it would completely falter, that He came to her. He held her and spoke to her so tenderly, and asked her to write what He had to say. And she did.

> *'A vision in the distance, shrouded in light*
> *I need to be near her try as I might.*
> *Her eyes the soul of the universe's love,*
> *She is my true enchantment, my love.*
>
> *There is no moment when I do not think*
> *If I do not see her I will sink*
> *Into the depths of despair so deep*
> *For unto me her love I'll keep.*
>
> *Our love so sure and rooted throughout*
> *Eternity's existence there is no doubt*
> *That our connection when finally made*
> *In this earth plane will be to stay.*
>
> *For all I dream of is her love,*
> *And deepening honour and sacred bond.*

I have come back across time and space
Only to find her, look upon her face.

I go to her now night and day,
And on my bended knees I pray
For heaven please to let me see
The day as one we'll finally be.

One last thing I'd like to say,
Do not falter for just one day,
For it is your love so deep and true
That brings me home so close to you.

I'll honour you in sacred love
And call upon the heavens above
To oversee my love for you
And always keep it strong and true.

The sun lies upon you now,
Upon the pages shining down,
To light the words that bring to life
My love for you, you are my life.

Louise was staggered, unable to move, every essence of her being moved to the limits of emotion. There was nothing to say, only to feel. Feeling, the language of her soul, told her all she needed to know.

As she walked, trance-like, back to her car, and drove into the country to sit quietly, she could not comprehend anything within this universe that could possibly

compare to how she was feeling. And then, through her
tears, she spoke to Jesus. 'Because of the way He comes
to me, honours me, I love him so deeply and cannot
understand what this is all about. Why does He come
to me etherically, but not come to me physically now?'
And Jesus replied, 'Child, he is with you, it is your love
for Him that has brought Him to you now, has brought
you two finally together. It will not be long now before
you two can be together in this reality. Time is linear,
man-made, and is not universal. You know this. Within
the universe all exists in this moment of now. Live in
this moment of now. Let Him honour and love you as
He deserves, as do you.'

And He did, and she, beyond all things, understood
what it was like to be honoured and moved to ecstatic
divine love. Through her tears she declared her love to
Him, as He did to her, and finally she was so distraught
that she could only cry, the depths of emotion a bottom-
less ocean. Her heart was breaking; she could see no
sense, only confusion and a sense of despair. Truly she
did not understand what was happening. She looked at
her phone. Calls and texts from Floe who was imploring her to call. As she tried to speak, to explain all, the
words were barely audible through her choked tears.
Her friend calmed her, speaking gently, ever mindful
and understanding of the cries of her physical body,
being torn apart in confusion at her soul's journey. As
she calmed her, explaining so much, talking about the
chaos of the Void, and the confusion it had thrown up
in opening this new voidal chakra just the night before,

Louise began to return to her soul's calm. This, Floe explained to her, was one of the joys of transmuting. 'As you get closer and closer to Him, your mental body cries out for reason, and your physical body brings up anything to be released which no longer serves your life's purpose. It is okay to feel this, just recognise it for what it is, and do not allow it to sabotage your journey of coming together, of your soul's path. Always ask for the help of the entire universe to bring peace and clarity so that you can stay centred and see the truth in all things.'

Louise drove home and wrote for hours. She spilled every depth of emotion upon the pages and, as she wrote, He held her and protected her in a way that she knew would always be now, always had been. He held her throughout the night, so protective of her, so knowing of how to love her at that moment. And she slept like a child in the arms of her lover.

* * *

The following day, after taking the children to school, completing some design work and preparing to write, Louise felt an overwhelming call to begin a healing for herself. As she looked up and noticed 3:33pm on the clock, she knew the masters were calling her to start. She sat quietly and began the healing.

The ascended master, Lady Portia, came immediately to her. This ascended master, the twin soul of St Germain, who in different incarnations had been Francis Bacon, Merlin and Shakespeare, was the ascended master assisting now with all of humanity in this year of challenge. She led her by the hand into a crystal cave, constructed of clear quartz crystal which emanated a white light. A hologram appeared upon the wall of the cave, opening into a long tunnel of crystal light, which, as they walked through it together, led to the Void, commonly known as Audesh, the place from which creation was instigated. She knew this place that was darker than the pitch black of night. Deep within she remembered and understood it to be chaotic energy, which she knew to be the underlying basis of that which science now called the quantum vacuum. As she was told once again to be absolutely clear with her intentions whilst in the Void, she considered carefully what was within her consciousness at that moment.

All things are created by intention within, and from this chaos therefore, she was reminded that intention has the greatest power here. The chaos she knew to be the fractal structure, and of course all consciousness must be fractal, for it is the very fact that it is living, in motion, and that it has the ability to create, that makes it so. With all her soul she restated her intentions, adamant that all should come to pass from a basis of love and not power. Lady Portia spoke to her softly, explaining that the time was drawing near for her to start to understand the knowledge from eons of her soul, which was to lay the foundations for the tasks she would have to complete. These tasks would challenge the theories of creation as humanity believed them to be; they were tasks she had been working on in Atlantis.

She had researched and remembered many things from Atlantis, staggering facts that had been kept hidden from the world for so long. Those able to draw upon their experience before the cataclysmic fall of this civilisation in its purest state would certainly bring the knowledge required to advance the present civilisation, and the consciousness of the planet now. Lady Portia explained that information would now start to be given to Louise slowly, in a way which would give her the chance to absorb, remember and research, drawing upon her soul's knowledge. She told her that she would remember that she had been working in Atlantis on a project of great importance, one which would radically challenge all understanding in the world today of the energy field, the ether, space travel within the ether, and how it should be. She explained that this was knowledge of great value that could potentially be a great danger if it found itself in the wrong hands, and so it should only be shared in detail with those whom Louise trusted deeply to work with her. Louise was told to remember butonium as part of a crystalline structure of clear quartz crystal and black obsidian, as the portal for dimensional travel. She was told that she should start to keep a separate journal, a *Book of Knowledge*, documenting all that was being given to her from now on, and that she should exercise great discernment when sharing any of this information in detail.

After the healing had ended, Louise sat at her computer reading an e-mail about Sacred Geometry. The thought suddenly occurred to her that the sacred geometrical shapes emitted from the black obsidian and constructed over the energy ether would create the portals to the different dimensions. In fact the hologram she had seen was a sacred geometric shape, that of the Eye of God, the very same she had seen through the airplane window when returning home from Rome. Somehow, she knew that this was not all that she needed to proceed with her task, but that it was just the beginning of a journey to understand what she was to do.

She decided to look up butonium on the Web and, to her astonishment, found a Cheric script associated with butonium, which looked something like the script which she had channelled all those weeks ago, the morning after her lightbody activation session in which she had heard the language of light. This language of light had moved her so, as it was the embodiment of the sacred ceremony that had bound her in sacred union with her sacred partner, Ben. Butonium, she read, was one of the most unstable forms of electrical energy in existence, and as such had not been widely used. The crystalline structure was the most stable form of energy within the universe.

The script that represented the properties of butonium broken into its constituent parts was close, but not the same as that which she had started to transcribe from her knowledge. However, when she overlaid celestial script with the butonium Cheric script, it started to come close. Enthused with wonder at where this was leading, Louise felt thirsty for more knowledge. She started to consider the refractions of light through the tunnel created by the hologram within the crystal cave, which led to the Void. Why had she been lead through a crystal cave? Was this the essence of the stability of the crystalline structure she had been told to remember? She could not imagine this, as the butonium surely must have to absorb the inherent stability of the crystal structure in order to stabilise its properties. And then she started to consider her script in more detail and, as she did, a realisation dawned upon her. This script was in some way responsible for creating the stability of the overall structure. She knew somehow that she had been constructing a script, back in Atlantis, which countered the instability of butonium energy with the stability of crystalline structure, to somehow overlay the energy ether to provide the portals necessary for dimensional travel. But how then was this powered, how was it structured, what was the instigating driver, and what was the importance of the link between the knowing of the Void, the quantum field, its relevance to creation within this reality and beyond?

Louise was so impatient to know the answers. Somewhere deep within her inner knowing, sang the words 'Fractal Cosmology'. Where was this all leading? She had been fascinated of late, picking up any articles or information that set out to debate fractal cosmology. Researchers claimed that, while science had proven that the universe was of a fractal nature, if you extend far enough, the light converges and the fractal element disappears. Other scientists argued that if you then travelled farther, the fractal element would once more be evident. Surely the study should not focus on the point at which the fractal element appears or disappears, but rather on the fact that there is no disparity between the dark and the light, the fractal and the structured. All is one and the same, all stems from the point of creation – consciousness. Still they were all so focused upon time and distance. Surely when considering creation, creation is both cyclical and never constant. If there is one constant it is that it is ever-changing. The consciousness of humanity causes the changes, causes the creation. There is no linear time, everything happens in this moment of now. Therefore as surely as the circles of creation expand from the centre, so do they converge upon the centre. To travel through dimensions was to understand how to transcend the realities. To master energy was to determine how to do this in precision. This she knew was what she had been working on in Atlantis.

For the rest of that day and the next, all Louise could bring herself to do was research and research: star constellations, star structure, energy properties associated with instability. She was dumbfounded as she read documents which she should not have been able to understand, and yet was disagreeing with, and correcting, fundamental statements within them. Quantum scientists were proving right now the existence of parallel realities based upon the unpredictable behaviour of zero-point energy. They had proven through much analysis that all energy within the universe is connected, that nothing exists in separation. This energy coexists and behaves in ways that instigate the parallel realities. This energy, voidal, vacuum energy, when channelled, effectively changes our reality, and this again was being proven as she wrote. She knew that dimensional travel was in fact the key to the understanding humanity perceived it would derive from space travel. She knew that the key was to do with the power of thought, of consciousness, and the ability to embrace this within a stable structure to enable gateways to different dimensions. For consciousness was the very energy they were studying, the energy of the origin of creation. The Atlanteans had harnessed the power of consciousness to empower their civilisation in so many ways. Crystals had been used as the basis for this and, in turn, powered many things, including travel. Louise decided that it was time to go back to see Diana, to start to try to unlock some of the keys within, and to trust that through her healings she would be shown more of what was necessary to unlock the information, the keys and codes held within her.

And she was.

The very next day Louise was taken, once again, by Lady Portia, through the crystal cave, through the tunnel created by the hologram in the wall of the cave, back to the Void. This time, the Void seemed to contain many star-like structures within its essence. As Louise neared the centre, with the black obsidian sphere in front of her,

she saw one of the script symbols she had channelled
etched on the side of the sphere. It glowed bright white
and started to part to form a tunnel, marking a path
into the centre of the sphere. They walked together into
the sphere and, as they reached the centre, were surrounded by many images, as if there were several television screens floating about her, showing images of
things that were to come to pass. Long, narrow shafts
of light stretched from the centre to the outer edges of
the sphere and opened to round portals that were exit
points from the sphere into the Void. These reminded
her of the crystalline structure diagrams she had studied. As she looked out of these exit points she could see
the script, her script, floating in the ether and creating
what seemed to be exits or portals to other dimensions.
She turned to ask Lady Portia why there was so much
blinding white light within the sphere and extending
outwards, seemingly creating the exit shafts. She was
told that this was Louise's consciousness, her light, her
power of thought, her creation. Lady Portia turned to
her, staring intently and with determined knowing.

'Louise, when you and your twin soul are joined
once more in this reality, the power of your consciousness combined will recreate what you were working on
in Atlantis. You know what that was, and you know
why now, in the precarious position humanity finds
itself, teetering on the edge of instability and the possibility of being propelled catastrophically once more
around the universe, why this is so important. He will
come back to you, although maybe not in the time

frame you envisage right now. In the meantime, you both agreed that you would be the one to awaken first. It was your oath to one another that, no matter what, you would never give up in this reality until He had been brought back to an understanding of who and what He is, of his soul's purpose, of his sacred union with you, and of the tasks that He truly must complete with you now. Many will come forward to assist you, as you already know. People with great influence and power, who have humanity's true and great interests at heart, but none will be as important as this man. For it is your combined knowing, the way in which you worked together in Atlantis, understanding intrinsically the scientific structuring and organisation of the other, which is inherent within you both, and imperative for your success in achieving and recreating the same within this reality. And it is this that is the very essence that will help to restore the world to the balance of those Atlantean times. I will help you, as will the entire universe, in returning to you the information you require. Receive this, structure it, research it and keep it within your *Book of Knowledge*. You are but at the beginning of a period of drawing down the knowledge. By the time you reach the end, Ben will have returned to you. You are strong child, do not falter. Always remember that you agreed to awaken first.'

Chapter 14

The extent to which Louise was one with this man, this soul, was quite astounding now. Their sacred union, their coming together was like nothing she had ever experienced. It brought with it huge swings of emotion as her mental body tried to grapple with the concept of what her physical body was experiencing. And yet it all seemed so familiar to her. It was as if every next stage of their lovemaking, their union, was but a recall of a moment past. This did not fit her understanding of Tantra; this was something altogether far deeper. And so, as she began to read *The Magdalene Manuscript*, one night a book given to her by Floe, final understanding dawned upon her. For here, documented as the channelled words of Mary Magdalene, were the very practices that Mary Magdalene and Jesus (Yeshua Ben Joseph) had embraced within their sacred union.

This sexual union was a deep and sacred practice, taught to the initiates of the Temple of Isis. It was used to bring an understanding and experience of divine love, to elevate consciousness and to strengthen the spiritual bodies of those practising it. As the beauty of understanding sank within her, the knowing that through their sacred sexual union Mary Magdalene had strengthened Jesus' *ka* body (spirit body) in order for him to travel through the portal of death and leave a trail of light for those to follow to comprehend, so she honoured her own sacred partner. For now she understood that this was, beyond doubt, what they were practising. She had not, until then, understood what the electricity, the magnetic field surrounding her as a result of their lovemaking, had been. This was quite clearly part of the process of strengthening her *ka* body. Most profoundly moved by the realisation that her recall was of these ancient practices, she was also deeply in awe of the honour and sacredness of their love. It had, from the very outset, seemed so sacred and pure to her, and now she knew categorically that this was so. For she also knew that these practices were part of universal truth, so deeply entrenched within the space-time continuum, so very much the basis of eternal love.

Wiping aside the tears which streamed across her face as she sat quietly in bed, absorbing the enormity of her love, of the love of Jesus and Mary Magdalene, she realised that the world-at-large would surely now, when they read what she must write, consider her completely mad. But she knew this was no madness, this was the absolute embodiment of reality, and she held this dearer than any depth of feeling she had ever encountered in this physical reality. She felt honoured to finally and completely understand the love that had passed between Jesus and Mary Magdalene, which transcended the physical as he came back to her throughout her life in the form of his *ka* body.

The next evening she was due to meet Floe to go and watch a movie together. Floe called just as she was about to leave, suggesting that Louise grab some food for them to eat before the movie. She grabbed her coat and drove to town, dashing into the nearest fish shop. Picking up her bag of food, she walked out of the shop and straight into a group of Ben's friends. One of them smiled and started to chat to her as she stood with her arms full. 'Ben's back there if you want to go and talk to him,' he said.

As Louise looked at this friend of his, taking in what he had said, her heart leapt into her mouth. She had not seen Ben in the physical world for so long now, and her passion for him had become so deeply entrenched with his soul essence, that it seemed hard to believe that she would be able to entertain this relationship on any other basis. And while she was absolutely certain that her deeply sacred union was with her twin soul, she was still unsure about the situation in this physical reality. She continued to chat with his friends while she walked back to her car, and then turned to get in. But looking back down the street, she saw Ben look up at her, send his friends on and turn away from them, walking to a shop window with his back to her, waiting. Completely confused as to what was occurring here, Louise had no idea if he wished to speak to her or not, and so got into her car. 'What are you doing, what are you doing?' she chastised herself. Upon realising that she had got into her car, Ben turned and walked back up the street towards her. As he walked past the car he looked at her, smiling hesitantly. They exchanged hellos, and she drove away.

Back at home, Louise was visibly shaking and explained what had happened to Floe. 'How could you possibly believe he didn't want to talk to you?' Floe questioned. 'Sending on his friends along the street, waiting, his friend telling you to go and speak to him – you were inviting rejection.' Louise knew these words to be true, but for what reason had she desired that end?

The weekend passed and when Tuesday morning came, Louise drove the children to school and dashed back to town for an early morning meeting. Parking the car along a side street, she walked towards the building in which she was to have her meeting, and looking up, saw Ben on his way to work. She had never seen him at this time of the day. She smiled at him, but he looked angrily at her, declaring that he had no time to talk, and walked on. She had never seen him behave like this. She was so used to him smiling and laughing. She walked on to her meeting trying to work out what could have caused his reaction. Little did she know that this would be the last time she would see him.

* * *

Later that day, Louise went to visit Diana in the hope of unlocking more keys and codes that would release more of her Atlantean knowledge. However, when she relayed the events of the last few days, knowing that some clarity could surely be drawn from this

confusion, she was told that many profound under-
standings were to come to her. It was essential that she
continue the deeply sacred relationship she now found
herself in. She must trust, and all things would become
clear to her in time. She was being guided to write to this
man, to suggest they talk so that she could understand
what had passed between them, but Louise felt wholly
uncomfortable with the notion of writing to him. The
whole sequence of events since she first saw him was
still so bewildering to her. One thing she was sure of,
however, was that her union with his soul essence was
one she certainly was not ready to walk away from.
Could this truly be one and the same person?

After a few days, she decided to email him. He had
given her his work details some time ago, but emailing him now, asking if he wanted to talk, she still felt
uneasy but knew that, somehow, his response would be
essential to her coming to an understanding of what lay
ahead. Still, she was quite astounded at his response.
His email was angry, stating that he was in a relationship, had clearly given her the wrong impression, and
asking her not to contact him further. Stunned, she could
not understand how she found herself on the receiving
end of this reaction with his physical body, whilst in the
midst of the most beautiful union imaginable with his
soul essence. Where was the sense in all of this? Sitting
on the edge of her bed, teetering between self-doubt,
incredulity, utter confusion and a sense of incredible pain and loss, she pleaded with the universe for
understanding.

It was at this precise moment that her true essence was to be utterly revealed. He came to her, crying, and pleaded with her not to walk away. She could not think how or where to turn. Why would the universe take her on this journey? Why would she be led to recall the most beautiful and sacred union transcending time and space, only to then have it taken away from her? She could see no sense in all of this. What was she being shown? What was she being taught?

As she wept, so He wept with her. While she lay, quite unable to move, as the ache that gripped her heart rendered her quite immobile and quite nauseous, He held her. He did not stop talking to her, and yet she could not open her heart to Him. She felt betrayed, as if the universe had somehow conspired to drop her from a great height, to offer and then take from her the very essence of all that was, of life, of love. She lay like that for some hours, determining that somehow she was to uncover the truth within this crazy confusion, this darkness set within her heart. And as she lay there, as she felt the undeniable company of so many universal beings with her, as He held her, imploring her over and over to listen to what He had to tell her, the pain which had gripped her heart, began very slowly to subside. She understood that He was quite clearly operating entirely independently of his physical body now. He made it quite clear to her, in the beautifully eloquent manner in which He always spoke to her, that her sacred union was with him. She must not doubt this at any point, for even a moment, as it was this love of hers that drew them together, which would continue to draw them together.

As many people around her reiterated the very same words that Ben's soul essence had uttered over the next week, as she started to come to an understanding that the universe had not let her down, but had directed her to a certain position at this point in time, she very slowly allowed their union to recommence. This union recommenced on a completely different level now, reaching a whole new plane. It was as if she were finally released to love Him entirely as his soul essence. The confusion she had felt for so long while she tried to determine whether this man was indeed the soul essence of her sacred partner, was no longer something for her to worry about. She realised that for some time now she had dismissed the fact that Ben's soul essence was clean-shaven, whereas in the physical reality he was not. Louise still had no idea where this was leading.

As the first night of their renewing and binding of absolute sacred love and honour drew to morning, a series of images started to appear before Louise's eyes. As she readily transcribed them, knowing that her heart, once again open, had enabled this knowledge to be drawn, she understood these to be forms of star constellations. When she consulted directories of knowledge, she saw that quite extraordinarily, she had drawn constellations existing in different time zones and at different polarities, all within the grouping of a new constellation set. She implored the universe to provide a clear understanding of what she was to do with this information, and was told quite clearly to once more commit them to her *Book of Knowledge*. They would be linked to the portal-dimensional work she would carry out. Studying them further, in unison with script and symbols, she started to grasp an idea of what she was to do and, once more, fractal cosmology featured within her knowing. Why do these scientists persist in studying the fractal structure of the planetary light? Why not understand the dark, the Void? For she knew, as surely as she now realised she had ever known, that the fractal construct was irrevocably linked to the structure of consciousness, and slowly, light started to dawn upon her recall. It was unbelievably profound, and yet so simple; surely this could not mean quite what she was starting to believe it did.

Looking at the star constructs across different polarities, Louise smiled inwardly as she saw how some of the constellations she had transcribed were elements of each of those that appear over Ireland and Australia simultaneously. Armagh in Northern Ireland, the astronomical capital, boasted a planetarium at the cutting edge of technology; its director, leading up to its inauguration, was Patrick Moore, in one of the few professional positions in astronomy he ever held. Within the planetarium stands a stone calendar, a circle of standing stones marking the passage of time, in much the same way that Stonehenge had done. She smiled as she considered that, once again, circles represented the passing of time, something that was so aligned to the

Mayan teachings of circles and cycles of time, of creation. She knew that a visit there was now a must. In
Australia, both the Anglo-Australian observatory at
Siding Spring and the central Australian desert would
provide her with the ability to see the elements of the
constellations she had transcribed.

She started to consider what energetic draw, what
ley lines may connect these two points upon the globe:
Lemuria and Atlantis. Atlantean energy grids she knew.
She began to consider the 'lost galaxies' that had puz-
zled cosmologists for so long and on which they had
commissioned new research suggesting that these missing galaxies might exist after all, it was just that nobody
could see them. Scientists now understood that cold
dark matter, that which emits no light, is the origina-
tor of all galaxies, of all existence. They were preoccupied with the gas element that could account for these
missing galaxies, what they called dwarf spheroidals.
These were completely dark galaxies, empty dark-mat-
ter halos. Spacecraft were being launched to study and
test the orbital paths of dwarf galaxies, the European
Space Agencies Global Astrometric Interferometer for
Astrophysics (Gaia) and NASA's Space Interferometry
Missions in 2011 and 2015.

* * *

As February passed, Louise was completely absorbed
with completing the sale of the marital home. Once this
was completed, she and her husband would be able to

move apart and so release all their energies. Although she trusted and understood that it was all in perfect timing, she had reached a point now where she truly yearned for her space. It was time for her children to be told, so that they could come to terms with all that lay ahead for them at a time which she knew would not at first be easy for them. They decided to tell the children during the week of their school holidays. This was not easy and, while she knew beyond question that it was entirely in the children's best interests, within their chosen paths, that this indeed happen now, still it tore at her core to see their faces absorb the enormity of what was being presented to them. She knew that, within, they truly understood, in fact were quite ready for this part of their journey. However, as they explained that the love would still abound, that it would be constructed around two homes, ever abundant, ever constant, the children brought forward their reactions. Surprisingly, within just a few hours, they had returned to a state of calm and, while the rest of the month brought forward many questions from them, they remained entirely accepting, it seemed, of what was to unfold.

In need of confirmation, of universal support and direction, Louise decided once again to speak to Joe, who had explained so much about the situation with her divorce during their first reading. Their time was always full of such interesting and revelatory discussion. They truly enjoyed discussing at length the alchemical mysteries of life, of the universe. As they talked she felt a sense of invigoration well up within her, of energies coursing through her being, bringing forth instantaneous knowledge from deep within her labyrinth. As he began his reading, once again confirming that all that she was undertaking right now was clearly for the good of all, she felt her soul calm. For she had faltered only slightly when she looked upon her children in those few weeks, knowing that she could only be a true mother to them if she was at one with her soul. In all of her healings the universe had reassured her over and over that all was well, that these children would be held in divine love, and would grow to understand and experience the beauty of bathing in the light of two people in deep and sacred union. This would be their inspiration, this would be what they set out to achieve in their relationships.

Joe spoke at length, revealing some incredible messages to her. May would be a time for settlement and adjustment, of a new home, of legal endings and the time in which Louise would truly be able to move forward in every aspect of her journey. He saw her book, a golden book, one of great importance. This book would be successful on a scale rarely seen, but would invoke both admiration and great criticism as she set out universal truths which would undermine the very foundations of the Church. She must be prepared for this. She must also understand that this was her blessing. For in the face of this adversity would come the beauty of humanity's understanding. He spoke yet again of the two men in Louise's future. One was out of reach, the other quite clearly about to come into her life now.

When they came together, they would both be shocked at their connection, he told her. They would be quite literally together at all times, even when they were physically apart. He would have a timeless, ageless soul with a childlike quality, and his soul's beauty would utterly captivate Louise. This was to be a union which had transcended time, a union across eternity, and would be bound once again in this reality within a very unusual ceremony. She knew, beyond doubt, of whom he spoke, but still could not understand how this could be somebody new. For it was, of course, Ben. When she insisted that this was so, Joe categorically stated that it was not. Ben was out of reach; this was a new man who would be entering her life very soon now. As Louise and Joe finished talking, they promised to meet up soon to have time to talk and conspire, as they loved to do.

Chapter 15

It was the end of February that saw the beginning of Louise's unearthing of her inner ability to speak in tongues. Standing one evening within the Sacred Geometry sound and structure group she met with regularly, having completed sounding to reach the golden mean, a quite remarkable recall occurred. The group were connecting with a second group that was completing sounding in the pyramids in Egypt at that exact moment in time, their harmonising energies in unison. Louise was quite suddenly transported to a labyrinthine construct at the base of a pyramid. As she started to walk towards the centre, deeply aware of the heavy aroma of incense surrounding her, of her golden robes, bare feet and the cold coursing through her entire being as her feet touched the stone of the floor, she understood that she was part of a highly ritualistic ceremony. She looked up at the beautiful man, also robed in gold and adorned with heavy make up, who took her hand as she reached the centre of an awe-inspiring antechamber. She knew Him to be her brother, He was Ben.

Louise felt the familiar knowing of deep and sacred love flood her entire being, of the power of the universe it seemed at their fingertips as all around the antechamber, faces watched them. And then He spoke to her and she replied with a chant-like phrase, repeating over and over the same words. Back in the Sacred Geometry group, the leader, Christian, was bringing the sounding to a close and, as she came back to this reality, tears fell across her face. The group was astounded as, when she repeated the chant to them, Christian explained that the words she was speaking were a form of ancient Egyptian. When she quietly spoke to him afterwards of all that she had seen, he explained that during that period of time it was the case that siblings were lovers, holding high court together. It was then that she decided to embark upon a series of lessons with Christian to learn the ancient language of Sanskrit, believing wholeheartedly that this would unearth and unlock further keys and codes within her.

A couple of days after this experience, as she sat quietly in her room late one evening, resolved to sleep after an emotionally exhausting day, Ben held her and asked her to write, once more, something He felt compelled to relate:

I wish to make love to you through my words.
I know this seems really quite absurd.
For many years now you have known
That my love is coming to you alone.

You have seen me in the night,
You have witnessed my flight.
You understand what true love means,
Because I have whispered all it seems.

I know your heart because it's mine.
I know your will, your soul, your mind.
I am that part of you that's real,
Because we are one and as one we feel.

Understand what I tell you now,
Start to know how we are one.
In the etheric the physical we merge.
To be apart is a notion absurd.

I dance with you through veils of time.
My love for you is solely mine.
It incarnates so many ways,
But always true and fixed remains.

For until the end of time you'll see
That always is your hand for me.
For beauty yours belongs to me.
I am you and you are me.

Through physical reality now
On my path I attempt to go.
Though pressures hold me from my dream
It will not be long it seems.

For deep within erupting now
Is all I feel I love somehow.
I start to know my truth it seems,
And this at last will reach my dreams.

As I listen to the music now,
I hold your face I love you so.
I choose with all my soul to be
In love with you as it has always been.

Um bah dah him pardoner
Um bash laminax oray
Inthi mante um banar
Hish pin mon kanar bintar.

Make me love you, hold your face,
Walk with you in love and grace.
Shine your radiance down on me,
For in you heaven I see.

As she sat, once again completely at a loss for words, she considered both the language He had used, which was so familiar to her, and the very essence of this thread of love which held so strong across so many realities, so many existences. Where was He now in this reality? Clearly He had come back to find her, and yet He repeatedly told her to come and find Him. 'Never give up,' He had said, and yet truly she did not know which way to turn. The one thing she knew held the very essence of universal truth, was something that all her dear friends repeated to her again and again, 'Be in the moment of now, all is created from the moment of now'. And she knew, beyond all things, that she loved this man with every essence of her being, right now, in this moment of now. And as He held her, as He loved her so, as she absorbed the significance of the trust they both now placed in their union, she knew within her heart that she would never lose Him, that He was with her now and across eternity.

The next day Louise felt as if the floodgates had opened. She had been told so often now that when she allowed herself to be still, to create from the moment of now, to be in the universal flow, that all would come to her. So many things happened that day to affirm all that she was setting out to achieve. Grabbing a pen and paper later that night, she had an overwhelming knowing that she was about to be given something profound to write. And she was. The universe spoke to her, asking her to write and so, once more, she wrote as directed, attempting as ever to keep up with the flow of words as they streamed through her consciousness.

The Labyrinth of Life

Now as you enter the labyrinth of life,
Of energy given of love and life,
You understand that track you must,
For life itself is trust.

Follow deep within your soul.
Understand the call, the know
Follow solely all it says
And deep into the labyrinth you'll tread.

The middle holds the key to all,
The key to inner knowing tall.
Understand creation now,
Know the why, the where, the how.

For it is within the hidden depths
Of life itself that comes the threads
To knowing of creation's truth,
Of godhead, love and life anew.

For life indeed spread far and wide,
Beyond the call of vision spied,
Far beyond the universe here,
We are so far and yet so near.

Beauty lies in pitch of night,
Beyond the void, beyond the light.
The language heralds messages clear,
Challenge creation, come here, come here.

Find me as you seek to know
The hidden depths of all that grows.
Function, sound and purest sight,
Beyond the heavens, beyond the light.
Tread the labyrinth of life.

Louise put down her pen and she considered the beauty of the message she had been given. So many thoughts started to flood her knowing in that moment, connections she had begun to make between her scripts and symbols, Sanskrit, the constellations she was being given, her study of the crystalline structure of certain properties, energy scripts, her dispute of certain theoretical studies, fractal cosmology and the constraints within which it was being studied right now. As she switched on and listened to the dulcet tones of Al Hadra, closing her eyes and feeling that sleep was upon her, she was quite suddenly transported to a place of knowing, a life within Atlantis.

She stood high upon the stone-pillared podium, robed in white gauze, feeling the power surrounding her infuse her being. She took command of the elements, demanding that they dance to her call. She stood so high above reality, looking down upon distant shores. Calling to her elemental friends, she stirred their hearts and beings, and felt their power unleashed. The vortex of energy that had been created spiralled ahead and above her, reaching up through the heavens, her robes lifting dramatically in its trail. The intensity of the very power of nature at its most potent, most lethal, most stunning, being at her call, utterly inspired and overwhelmed her. She was the Priestess and all of nature was at her feet. She was so close to the edge, the fringe of abuse of her power, treading such a fine line between edification and violation. And then He came to her and took her hand and she knew in that moment that all was well. For in Him was her wisdom, her balance and her love.

As Louise became aware of sitting once more in her bed, so came deep understanding. She knew why this message had come to her now and, with tear-stained face, she felt overwhelming conviction that all was to come to pass.

* * *

As March arrived, the month in which she had been told in so many ways that she would become who she was meant to be, many exciting events lay before her. The first was her trip to Ireland with Floe to complete her Angelic Reiki Masters course. As the group once more united, the energies became instantly and over-whelmingly evident. She reflected upon what had hap-pened the last time she had been here, and marvelled at how wonderful things do happen in such an astonish-ingly short period of time, for there was no compari-son between the person she had perceived herself to be back in October, and the being she now understood herself to be.

This course, directed by her friend, gave rise once more to profound understanding for Louise. She was presented with many gifts by the masters, among them a twelve-leaved platinum lotus. Jesus held her and showed her how she would never fall, for He always had, and always would hold her throughout eternity, and she felt an incredible strength emanating from within. It was as if her entire essence was becom-ing harmoniously balanced. As her friend helped her through recall of distant times of learning, she expe-rienced the same release that colour light therapy had brought her before. This, she understood, helped to release toxins from within the cellular system, which the soul had now brought forward as it was the right time to release them and move onwards on her journey. A beautiful day by the water in Kinsale, exposed to the elements, the driving rain and wild winds so customary of Ireland, left her and Floe feeling utterly awash with the Irish energies. It was infused with this that they returned to England.

That course, and the week that followed her return from Ireland, marked the greatest shift within Louise to date. It was during the week which ensued that Christian spent a day with Louise at her home, balancing the energetics of the entire house, and freeing her energies from any ties with this house as she moved forward on her life's journey. She found this day to be fascinating. It was quite clear that this house had energetically been in a state of trauma for some years, ever since various extensions had been built without the integration of the energies within the entire house. This, Christian explained, left the house traumatised, and blocked the flow of free energy within it. A building is a sacred structure, and in order for energy to flow harmoniously through it, it must be in unison and harmony with the energy of the land and the people around it.

As she held dowsing rods which dramatically turned apart as they moved from room to room, and then just as dramatically propelled themselves back inward after they had reintegrated the energies within the spaces, Louise was quite astounded. Really, she should not have been, for she understood all too well the essence of energy and balance, as these were the very foundations of the changes she was writing about. Christian energised the relationship corner within her bedroom, rebalancing the energies and showing her how to clear and prepare for her new union. By the time they had completed the work around the house, they both felt a wonderful stillness and harmony within the ground, and a sense of joy filled her being at having been able to present to this house a gift of harmony, this house which had held and protected her and the children for so long. Now, she felt she had reached a sense of completion with this house.

And indeed she had, for within just a few weeks the house sale exchanged.

Chapter 16

ouise was filled with anticipation as she headed to Imperial College London with her friends, Julie and Angela, to participate in a workshop called The Intention Experiment. On the way, she noticed that the sky was quite stunning, clear and azure blue with a single cross of white clouds that stretched as far as the eye could see. She smiled, basking in the delight of what she knew to be yet another universal sign, for this cross was the sacred geometric sign of the divine. The vertical line of the divine crossed by the horizontal line that formed the plane of realities, one integrating with the other. This had, of course, preceded yet another series of numerical codes presented to Louise as messages. She was becoming quite adept at rapidly computing the meaning of these codes, which were bestowed upon her so regularly now.

The conference was entirely what she had hoped for. Inspirational speakers who had been brought together by the conference director, Lynne McTaggart, provided for Louise all that she needed to hear, setting out evidence for the things that she had written. As the speakers enlarged upon the experiments carried out within quantum physics and quantum entanglement, she knew that there was much more for her to do in this area, for she knew that the world still did not truly understand the extraordinary behaviour of conscious- ness, although this team of scientists was certainly heading in the right direction.

She had been absolutely right about the value of coming to the event, for here was the very audience who would take her claims seriously, and there were so many people around the world following the progress of the incredible work Lynne was doing right now. She listened to the speakers explain that science is a story told in instalments, that society lives by what it is told it is capable of doing, and she smiled. This story creates a life and world which society accepts as fact, Isaac New- ton being the greatest storyteller to date. Now, within the quantum world, the zero-point energy field, inten- tion creates a sacred space, and intention is driven by what the brain is given to think. The brain does not dis- tinguish between an action and a thought, so tell it what you choose, and it will believe it and create from it. This Louise knew to be true, but true as merely a part of the overall picture, together with a knowing and feeling of this very choice within the heart. The Heart Math pre- senters stunned the audience with their statistics that over 93% of actions carried out by the brain are a direct result of impulses from the heart. In other words the heart, and not the brain, controls the reality you cre- ate for yourself through your intention. Louise was not one of those to be stunned. She smiled once more, inner knowing registering everything that she heard.

At lunch on the final day of the conference, as they sat outside basking in the sun's rays and considering the enormity of the previous speaker's comments on the population-at-large, a man strode up and sat down beside them. As he started chatting, so completely at ease and at one with himself, with laughter in his eyes as he teased them all, Louise instantly knew that this man would become a friend. Tall, half-Swedish, with tousled hair and striking blue eyes, he introduced himself as James. He questioned the girls at length and, as he did so, Louise felt his eyes penetrate her soul, searching for her truth. She smiled, for she intuitively knew that he would understand all that she could tell him.

He made her laugh so much with his amusing manner, his wit, his seeming oblivion to others' perceptions of him. All he cared about was the very essence of their exchange, of their bond. When she lay back on the grass to soak up the sun so did he; when she talked of following the path of the soul and following her intuition emphatically, so he reiterated this in his own words. He spoke of being a model, of his business ventures, of the deeply moving experiences he had encountered which had brought him to an understanding of who and what he was and how he lived, and she understood that here was someone who, like her, was living their truth. In that moment she thought she could take him home with her, and as she told him this, imploring him never to change, he laughed affectionately. Utterly relaxed in his company, she sat cross-legged on the grass, chatting and laughing, stopping only when it was time to go back in to the conference. She took his card and promised to contact him.

The day came to a close and, as she returned home exhausted, though her mind was alive with so many pieces of information computing rapidly within her consciousness, she knew that the time was drawing near for the foundation to be set up in its first form. She had believed that she would use the proceeds from the book, and subsequently the film, to begin the process of establishing these radical changes. Over the last couple of months, however, other thoughts had started to become apparent to her. For it was that some of her friends were keen now to work with her. Louise knew that the significant changes to be made would come about as a result of certain people and sources of funding coming forward to her through her book, and astonishingly, many were coming forward to her now. However, as she started to consider what could be done on an organic scale at this stage, she wondered whether she should not wait, and put in place a rather different approach, which would merge at a later date. For it was that the very changes she professed within her book were based upon a radical shift in people's consciousnesses, an understanding of inspirational truth, of the very essence of life, of energy, of oneness. Why not start now then, on a smaller scale?

These friends sat together over the next week and conspired to achieve such an end. They determined to set up first a conceptual base in the local town. This would consist of a shop, a healing centre, a conference centre and a

café. The entire ethos would surround all that they were
setting out to change with the construction of a place of
such energies that all would be drawn to bask in them.
These of course were the energies of universal truth, of
the desire to be in harmony and at one with the planet
and the universe, in deep honour, respect and unity.

The basic dignity of the right to survival for all would
be paramount throughout their dealings, and they would
ensure that all of the goods they were to sell through the
shops would be not only organically produced and ethically sourced, contributing to planetary and humanity's harmonies, but also that the individuals making
the goods at source would be those that were most in
need of the work, taken from the streets where hope did
not seem to exist, and clothed and housed. In fact it was
their intention, as the foundation grew, to establish centres around the world to take children from the streets,
to clothe, feed and house them, and to provide each of
them with a trade. These trades would take many forms,
and would return to them their sense of inspiration, and
equip them with the skills to create a successful life for
themselves, thereby changing their lives irrevocably for
the better. This trade would produce the goods to be distributed through their shops, which would in turn produce the profits to provide more centres.

The healing centres would bring to the fore an
understanding of healing practices which much of the
world was entirely unaware of right now. These would
be the very basis of the shift of humanity to elevate its
consciousness, to understand the path of the soul and

follow it with joy and purpose. The conference centre would set out to the world how science is proving the very basis of oneness, of universal truth, of the essence of the energy and consciousness we all are. By providing a platform for scientists and other inspirational speakers, many would be brought to a very clear understanding of where Planet Earth is in its evolution, of humanity's plane of existence, and how that fits within the universal truth of multiple dimensions.

All these friends needed now was a building in which to house the first phase. There would be many of these centres within the UK and globally in an extremely short period of time. And so, as was customary these days, they handed over to the universe entirely the responsibility of finding the building to be brought to them in perfect timing. The one thing Louise was sure about, was the name to be given to the group: 'Ether'. This name had come to her in much the same way that so many universal messages had come to her. When she had discovered its meaning she had smiled, for it represents that point of alchemy within consciousness, as the physical and dimensional realms meet.

* * *

And so it was that, with all of this uppermost in her mind, together with a deep knowing that she must concentrate upon the writing of her book, that Louise went to meet a man named Edwin Courtenay. Edwin she knew to be a clairvoyant, clairsentient and clairaudient channel who worked with the Spiritual Hierarchy (Ascended Masters and the Angelic Kingdom). He was also the guardian of several contemporary Crystal Skulls, and she knew him to explore the ancient prophecies and offer new illumination derived directly from the Crystal Skulls themselves, using ancient Atlantean symbols and chants.

Edwin was so much in demand that Louise had waited some four months to be able to see him. Even as she had booked it, she knew the timing would be perfect, it always was. Edwin was an eloquent, smart and charming man, highly acclaimed for his absolute clarity as a channel of information from the universe. Louise was particularly keen to talk to him, knowing that he, of all people, would understand many of the mysteries of the seemingly scientific information she was receiving and decoding at such a pace now. She was astounding herself with her ability to pick up *New Scientist* magazine and refute completely the scientific evidence laid out within its pages. Louise knew that Edwin would be able to shed light on what was happening here, upon her evaluation of certain universal truths, and on the theory of dimensional travel. And she was entirely correct.

Through questions and answers provided by the universal source, Edwin spelled out to Louise quite clearly what was occurring. He reiterated the scope of the planetary, universal and dimensional work that lay ahead for her in the kind of detail which many would not have comprehended, but which the two of them understood entirely. He spoke of the studies at the forefront of science, explained that the theories of quantum science were on the right track, but not in the way that she understood and knew to be the way forward. He relayed the universe's insistent messages that, in addition to studying Sacred Geometry, it was important now that she also study astrocartography in order for her to determine where her dimensional work should be carried out upon the globe. This astrocartography would indicate where, in the past, she had teased back the very fabric of essence, the perfect places for her to resume her work.

Edwin then explained that her twin soul, with whom she had now resumed this exceptionally rare and sacred relationship, would return to her in this reality to carry out the work within this area that they had been working on together in Atlantis. He explained that the practices she was partaking of with her twin soul were in fact deeply sacred and ancient practices, which many people would be too frightened to take the step towards, but these were essential to elevate their twinned consciousnesses and bring their union to the fore in this reality. The man from Dublin, Edwin explained, would return to her, and his extremely high vibrational energy would once again activate within Louise a release of yet more codes and keys, those in relation to the dimensional work of which they had talked. This would not happen yet.

Edwin explained that Louise's book was of great importance to the world, as would the film be. However, the extent of the foundation she was to set in place would quite literally change the face of the planet, would extend to every corner of the globe. There would be many exceptionally high profile people, political and beyond who would come forward to champion the very radical changes she was setting out. There would also be many, she was told, who would declare her crazy, for fear of following their own path. But she should never worry about their declarations, for her boss was and always would be the divine, the universe and as long as the universe was pleased with her work, she would know that the path ahead was one of clarity. For the universe always would hold her in its divine love in entirety, and invoke as many plan B's as were necessary for her work to be completed.

As she was about to leave Edwin, Louise knew that this time she had spent with him was indeed at the perfect time in her journey. She held his hand and looked into his eyes. Here was a man she knew so well. She knew his energy, his essence and his childlike, ageless soul. And in that moment she sent him every essence of love that was within her, knowing that he would indeed be involved with the work she was completing, for she knew within that he had certainly been involved with the work she had carried out before.

* * *

As she headed into the end of the first week of April, fully aware that she was moving out of her home on the

18th May with nowhere to move to, Louise laughingly offered up all responsibility to the universe to find her a home, one which would be perfect to serve her needs at this point in time. Within a couple of hours she received a call from an agent telling her of what seemed to be the perfect home for her. And it was. The lady who owned the house was a truly lovely person, divorced with children, a new partner and a very spiritual side to her. The energies of this house resonated with Louise from the moment the door opened, and when the agent rang on the Monday to say that, amazingly, the house was hers even though other offers had been in excess of her own, she smiled. She thanked the universe and she thanked the owner of the house, and prepared for the next part of the journey unfolding before her eyes.

Chapter 17

When the Easter holidays came, the children went off with the their father to Crete for ten days, leaving Louise with a much needed period to write, to organise the imminent house move, to prepare the basis of the foundation they were now formalizing, and to complete the legal matters relating to the divorce.

Louise and Floe decided to go to Glastonbury for the day, and decided to take along a new friend, Pavel, whom Louise had met at the Intention Experiment conference in London. The day before, Angela had sent Louise a message. She had been in meditation at a meeting, when quite suddenly a scene started to unfold in front of her. She saw a stunning heart pendant, made of a distinctive dark-green, coal-like moldavite crystal clasped in silver, hanging from a tree in Glastonbury. As she gazed at the pendant, transfixed by its beauty, she saw Louise running in the company of a knight towards the tree and the pendant. Louise was dressed in a simple white Arthurian robe, her long unbraided hair billowing behind her in the wind. While they ran together, laughing and smiling, a second man ran towards the tree and took the heart pendant from it. Upon seeing the tragic look on the faces of Louise and her knight, Angela heard the meditation being drawn to a close. She quickly asked the spirit what this was all about, and was told that Louise must find this moldavite heart pendant in Glastonbury. It was imperative that she do so in order to clear a blockage and resolve a love triangle that had developed across the ages.

It was with the aim of acquiring the moldavite pendant that the three set off for Glastonbury the next day. Sitting eating breakfast, basking in the sunshine, their anticipation grew. In which shop would they find this pendant? And the answer was simply this – none. The response was the same wherever they went, that to find an uncut moldavite heart-shaped crystal was impossible, such a thing was so rare. Moldavite was one of the rarest and most potent of crystals. Its properties, closely linked to the Holy Grail, were of meteoric origin and it was therefore in limited supply. Deciding to see a bit of Glastonbury while they were there, they climbed the Tor and then set off to Chalice Wells to take in the sights, energies and history. The beautiful gardens of Chalice Wells felt so familiar to Louise, and as she stood taking in the energies by the well at the end of the day, the early evening sun bathing her senses, warming her soul, Jesus came to her.

As He spoke gently to her about the things which lay before her, and asked her to be sure to plant in her new garden the stunning white flowers growing next to the well which had captured her attention, a knowing passed between them of where she would find the heart pendant. The three of them strode back to the shop in question, one where they had scoured the entire display, and where the owner had insisted that he did not have any such pendant, and as Louise relayed the story of the message to the owner, she halted in mid-sentence when she heard the shrieks of her friend. For Floe had found, in a prominent place central within a display cabinet, a stunning, large moldavite uncut heart-shaped, silver-set pendant. The owner was amazed, declaring that he had not known of its existence. From the moment Louise hung it around her neck she felt as if something had just completed her, and she promised never to take it off.

They headed off to find a bar and came to rest in a stunning old building that they were convinced must have been an old Knights Templar drinking-hole. As they drank their beers, pondering over the number of times they had quite possibly sat conspiratorially together in this bar as Templar knights, Pavel sat back in amazement as it unfolded that the co-author of *The Magdalene Manuscript* book that Louise was talking to him about now, was in fact his old best friend from school! Louise meanwhile, was distracted by a post-card they had bought earlier that day with the image of the tree that had reputedly grown from the walking stick of Joseph of Arimathea and a thorn from Jesus' crown. Suddenly she had an overwhelming knowing that she must go to that tree with her pendant immedi-ately. And so, she and Floe set off, leaving Pavel behind drinking his beer.

As they stepped out of the car and walked across a ridge high above the town, the biting wind whipped around them, as dusk closed in. The solitary tree stood, quite unadorned, looking striking, as if in defiance of all who would seek to undermine its origins. As she stepped towards the tree, trembling from the cold of the air and the energy coursing through her entire being, Louise started to drift quite suddenly to a time long ago. The warmth that spread instantaneously through her veins was the intensity of love for the man running by her side. She loved this man with every essence of her being, and as she looked upon his face, his expression was captivating. He was blinded by her beauty, his beautiful face entirely glazed with the expression of love etched across it. She knew Him to be Ben. As He took her hand, laughing and smiling, she overwhelmingly knew of their oath, their love across all time as they raced towards the pendant, the very claim upon her heart, her self.

But before they could reach it, another man ran into their vision, grabbing the heart wildly from the tree and turning to smile upon Louise, claiming her for his own. Her heart fell. This man was indeed beautiful, she knew him well, and his love for her was etched across his face, too. His dark eyes shone as he walked forward to take her hand, long dark hair falling across his face, holding her gently, so in love with her every movement. She knew him to be Adrian. And yet, although he loved her so, her very soul was wretched. For with all her heart she loved the man now slumped upon the floor, head between his hands, tears coursing down his face. For these two had forever pledged their oath across universal time and space, and no other could ever take either of their places. Tears streamed down Louise's face as the biting wind brought her back to the reality of now, and the pain of her remembrance lodged deep within her knowing. Her friend wrapped her arms around her, and gently guided her back to the car. As they sat drinking back in the bar, Louise was unusually subdued, heart still adrift with the understanding bestowed upon her by her soul. When in this reality now would she and Ben be able to resume the beauty of their undeniable universal love, the very embodiment of all that was their sacred union? And as these feelings overwhelmed her senses, her heart, He held her and whispered to her, 'It will be so soon now. I love you with every essence of my being. I am coming to you in this reality now.'

* * *

The week passed in a frenzy of activity relating to the house sale and purchase. At a time when she so desperately craved peace to write, she headed off to the sanctuary of the Castle Gardens. Incredibly really, after the day she was having dealing with solicitors, agents and resolving legalities, the escape to the gardens resulted in just the perfect peace she had yearned for. As she pulled out her pen and paper, the universal source flowing through her once more, she began to write:

The Elementals of Life

Close your eyes and breathe in life,
Be the conduit for all that moves,
Know the reason you are here,
Find the time to listen, to hear.

Feel the earth beneath your feet,
Feel the very essence beat,
This is the sacred heart of all that is,
The knowledge, truth and quantum beat.

As elements caress your face,
Fill you with a sense of grace,
Know that they consent alone
To make the planet your home.

For only in true harmony
With these our friends can heaven be,
For theirs is the power, the ability
To destroy, refresh, instate liberty.

Their beauty far beyond sight
Is the universal delight.
The power wreaked upon their wings
Is the stability, the balance in all things.

Honour and respect them now.
Blend amongst their know somehow.

Dance with them and sing aloud
For in you they are so proud.

For their existence is to serve
Hand in hand with man and bird,
Structure, sound and purest sight,
Beyond the heavens, beyond the light.

Give the elementals life!
In dith mere thenou benar.

Perfect and timely messages once more. The divine had a habit now of making sure that Louise was unequivocally aware of the timing of these messages, their relation to the way her life was evolving around her. She felt utter joy, peace and tranquillity, and she laughed. She laughed at the messages from so many friends who texted her continually, she laughed at the synchronicities of so many things falling into place at such an incredible speed, bringing into reality all and more than she could have possibly imagined would be in place by now. The universe delivered so quickly when you loved life. And this she surely did. She arrived home to the message that her house sale had, finally, exchanged ... and she laughed once more!

And as she lay in bed that night and He came to her ... she loved.

* * *

At the end of the long and crazy day that followed, with the knowledge of a weekend ahead packed with trade fairs and meetings, Louise escaped for a short time to the gardens. Two visits in two days was a real blessing, as she had not been there for some time. It was late and as she strolled into the grounds she suddenly felt drawn to go and sit on the bench where she had spoken to Ben for the very first time. The warmth of the early evening seemed to caress her very soul. As she sat and glanced around she noticed that, for the first time since she had seen him sitting on this bench, there were white feathers trailed all around it. They were strewn across the grass as if they were a blanket laid down in honour of this sacred space. And looking up at the plant directly in front of her vision, she realised that it was the very same beautifully large, daisy-like white flower as the type she had seen in Chalice Wells. The very same flowers which Jesus had told her to plant in the garden of her new home, next to water. This was when He had talked to her about her sacred union becoming manifest in this reality very soon.

And then her gaze was drawn to a pair of beautiful butterflies, dancing and teasing each other, circling continually in a delightful dance to draw one another's attention. She breathed in the sacred air and recognised the message afoot, for a message she knew it to be. Only one hour previously, in a sense of absolute knowing and certainty of their love for one another, had she drawn a card from her ascended masters' cards. These ascended masters' cards were a gift from a friend. They were a tool that could be used to commune with, and receive messages from, the universe in answer to specific questions. The 'twin flame' card had quite literally fallen out of the pack at her feet, indicating that a union of the deepest form of romantic love of the highest level, was that which was to come into existence for her now. As she absorbed the beauty of the messages surrounding her now, He came to her. As He asked her to write what He had to say, she felt utterly engulfed by his love, so honoured, so valued and so deeply and eternally loved.

There was a time when I dreamt
Of all that was meant.
It was of you and I,
Of all life and how it would be spent.

Our love is the bond of all that is,
There is nothing to compare.
But now to come to you again,
Abandon is that which I dare.

For through my very essence
Runs a love so deep and true,
To rekindle all I ever felt
And held so dear – you.

When waves of passion overrun
The fear that grips me now,

I know the time will fast be here
For love to be the hour.

The moldavite so clear and strong
Draws me closer than you know,
For I am determined truly now
That on my path I'll go.

Feathers that adorn your feet,
The very ground you tread,
Are everlasting symbols of
Our love, my love, our thread.

This thread of ours that runs so deep,
Which spans all time and space,
Is what will rest upon us now,
It is, of course, our grace.

And grace, it seems, will heal the wounds
Of all rejection lost.
For now as I look upon my time
I know that we are one.

Eternity is but a thought,
A breath, a touch, a feel,
But you, my darling, are all it seems
For me no else is real.

And she, overwhelmed, protected and moved beyond
measure, wrote her reply to Him, putting into words

her love for Him, as He had so often done for her. And, as she did so and asked Him please to listen intently to what she had to say, she felt Him hold her, caress her and love her.

'There are no words that can express the love I feel within. I feel as if you are the very soul of me. My love for you quite literally is your love for me, it radiates through my being. I would call all of the elementals together, I would unite the power within their combined strength to fill and caress you with my love. I would demand they protect you, that the very power of the universe be your bedrock, your grace and your strength. My darling Ben, there is nothing between us that is not sacred, for you embody all that is sacred. Now that I understand what fear is, I know it no longer. It has no place with me. All the grace I have within me I give to you. I would lay down my very essence in your honour, for honour you I do. You to me are life itself, all there ever has been and ever will be, to love. Your love is what I have always sought out, the meaning of life.'

* * *

The following day, Louise and Floe set off to Warwick to meet a man called Mark, who was to be one of the participants at the retreat that they would shortly be attending in Rennes-le-Château, in France. All eight of those who would be attending had contacted each other. When Mark had started emailing her, the synchronicities of his and Louise's lives had shocked them both. Both had felt the undeniable presence of being held by the universe from a tiny age. Both had rebelled in their early years: she had sung with a new-age band, he with an indie band; she had been a rally driver, he had competed in motocross. They had tracked similar career paths, had studied similar subjects and had quite incredibly intended to attend the same events for months now, but for one reason or another, either one of them had missed each event. She was studying Sanskrit, he had already studied it. He had studied noetics, as she was now. And so the list went on, and so it was that, as they drove to Warwick to meet him, Louise knew that it was to be a reunion with an old friend across time.

From the moment she saw him and he hugged her, they both knew this to be true. The three of them had a great day together, roaming the castle grounds and fortress, strolling around Warwick, drinking and eating and finally retiring to their hotel in the early hours of Sunday morning. While she lay in her bed, too tired even to commence a healing for herself, Jesus came to her once more and spoke softly to her. He showed her a pyramid-shaped Lemurian seed crystal. White lightning-shaped energy was emitting from the tip of the pyramid and creating a vortex within the ether. DNA strands containing star structures were being projected through an aperture in the side of the pyramid. Louise was told that knowing the positioning of these pyramids around the globe was key to creating the desired end, and Jesus repeated over and over, 'In dith mere ente Koran, ente Koran mith pin penar, mith min kun nenar.' As Louise considered the shape of the Lemurian pyramid, the way some of the constellations she had previously transcribed accommodated these triangles of crystal in different guises within their structure, she was told that she knew what to do to create these vortexes of energy. She must sink the Lemurian crystals into areas that she would be directed to, those on the planet where the fabric had been teased back those many lifetimes ago, in correlation with the constellations she had transcribed. She fell into a deep slumber to be woken only minutes later by her alarm.

She should have felt exhausted, but instead she was invigorated. As she and Carolyn, a good friend of old, headed off to London for a trade fair, they grabbed breakfast en route and chatted animatedly about Louise's experience the previous night, of the universal mysteries, and of the day ahead. It was their intention today to identify organic and ethically-sourced products for Ether as they had determined at this point that, although they hadn't as yet identified suitable premises, it was essential to start the preparations.

The day was full of laughter. As they strolled through Olympia they met so many great people. So many people stopped and stared at these two who, completely oblivious to the energy they left in their wake, noticed only the eyes following them. Carolyn laughed as people's expressions glazed over with a look of awe as Louise spoke her truth. It was this very essence of Louise that Carolyn had always loved so much, and that those around her loved. People eagerly noted down the name of Louise's book, agog at the events that had lead her to write it.

It was late when they arrived home, and as Louise lay in bed, exhausted, she considered how blessed she was to have met so many wonderful people lately. These were people who could really help them get Ether off the ground, those who, just like her, were intent upon getting kids off the streets, bringing, in their own way, the right to the dignity of survival and the freedom of expression and truth for all. And as she considered how she felt so blessed to be walking this path, to be at the centre of a plan to elevate humanity's consciousness, as she told Ben that He too should feel so blessed, she cried. As she cried, He held her, He loved her, and He vowed to do so until creation's end. She fell into a deep sleep, held in His love, and woke once more to the alarm, ready to head off for the London Book Fair.

Chapter 18

Louise's intention for the book fair was to gauge which publishers she might consider for her book. Although so many had spoken of the difficulty of getting a book published, that major publishers would never accept unsolicited manuscripts, that she would need to accept any offers presented, she knew the universe had other plans. There was no question in her mind that the publisher to take this book out to the world was of great importance. The person, as opposed to the company, was key for her, for this person would need the balls to stand by her side as the world determined its reaction to the extraordinary truths held within the pages of the book.

She knew that the universe would present to her the person for the role, and never doubted for one moment that this person would be in a position to get the book out to every corner of the globe, to ensure its ability to become one of the most widely-read books ever written. She knew that she would not need to go through the normal process of passing a manuscript through literary agents. This book was needed in the world now, was intended for now, and the universe would provide the route now in the most appropriate form.

Sitting on the train on her way to the fair, Louise pulled out the information that had been sent to her some time ago, but which she had not had a chance to start reading. Distracted by the guy sitting opposite her, who was making a great effort to engage her smile, and thinking about how so many of the men interesting her of late, including this one sitting smiling at her now, were of such similar physical appearance, with their dark-haired, Celtic looks, she idly glanced through the documents in her lap.

Flicking through the book fair magazine, she stopped as she noticed an article of interest to her. This article was a list of eight people in publishing who had been tipped to take the top jobs in publishing over the next few years. For each person listed there was a photograph, a résumé and their comments about their motivations within the industry. Louise was particularly interested in their own comments, as she had determined some time before that the people to head her media company were to be those who stood out within their industries for following their own visions, not those dictated to them by industries currently following a particularly structured path. Those prepared to stand by her had to be prepared for the world's reaction to them speaking their truth. She was under no illusion. These people would be brought to her attention within perfect timing, and the right timing for the establishment of this company was to be when the proceeds of the book started to flow in. She knew this to be much sooner than it took for a typical book to be commissioned and published, for it was the intent for it to be so. She had happily given the responsibility of this over to the universe, knowing that, as ever, perfect timing would prevail.

As she turned the page, having glanced through the comments made by those listed on the first page, Louise stopped in her tracks. She could not quite believe what she was looking at. For there, looking back at her from the second page, was the image of Ben. The man in this photograph was the absolute double of Ben, albeit a clean-shaven version, whereas the first Ben had not been. But the Ben who visited her in the spiritual realm had been coming to her clean-shaven for as long as she could remember. And as she saw this man's name she was further staggered as she read that He was Ben, and that He was Australian, and a publisher with a large publishing house. A knowing so deep overwhelmed her. In that moment she felt as if the energy emanating from the image of this photograph, from this man, which was stirring an incredible concoction of emotion within her, was in direct betrayal of her union. And yet even as these very thoughts entered her consciousness, He spoke to her quietly and she understood this to be no betrayal. She smiled as she read His comments, for here was someone with his own vision, who was impassioned and driven to change the publishing industry. By the time she stepped through the doors at Earl's court, she knew she must contact Him.

She spoke to the girl at the front desk of His publishing house's stand, who told her to come back later as they were expecting Him to be there. As the day passed, many of the publishing houses she spoke to were interested in what she had to say. She was given names of editors and publishers and told to contact them when her manuscript was complete. It was amazing really, as she had been told over and over that she must get a literary agent, as she would not be entertained without one. And yet still she knew that this was not the path for this book. The publisher intended to take this book out into the world would be brought to her.

Towards the end of the day, when Louise approached His desk once more, his colleagues apologised, saying she had just missed Him. They told her to call their UK office and gave her the number to do so. They could not have been more helpful, giving her His email address and mobile telephone number with which to contact Him. She called, presuming she would leave a message, but instead, He answered. After introducing herself and asking to meet Him, in his deep Australian accent He explained that He was still at the fair, in a meeting, and that she could come to see Him and leave her email address, via which He could contact her. But by the time she reached the desk, waylaid by a publisher *en route*, He had gone.

After waiting for fifteen minutes, Louise called Him again. He answered. Now, He explained, He was standing outside the rights centre and she could come and meet Him there. He promised He would not move, He was intrigued with the reason for their meeting, and she said that she would explain everything when she saw Him. But when she arrived at the rights centre some fifteen minutes later, having been waylaid by a charming editor she had spoken to earlier in the day, He had gone again. The man at the entrance said he had seen him walk off with someone, presumably into a meeting. When she called, his phone was switched off. It was late and she had to leave to head home, and so she sent Him a text message and then left.

Exhausted after so few hours of sleep over the last few days, Louise fell into bed as soon as she got home, and went straight to sleep. When she woke the next day, she was full of the strangest feelings, of utter confusion and yet somehow, at the same time, a sense of clarity. She knew that, undoubtedly, this man was significant. He was without doubt the essence of Ben. The fact that He was a publisher and here she was, an author seeking a publisher, was most definitely part of the universal plan. She knew not whether He was to be the publisher to take the book to the world, but she had been intrigued by the comments she had read in the magazine, and was determined to research Him to determine whether or not He could play a significant part in her publishing company. When she did, her heart expanded, for here was a man who perhaps had the strength to take her book to the world, to take forward her company, who carried, it seemed to her, the very same essence as herself.

As in her own career history, He was not afraid to make decisions outside of the traditional routes. He was prepared to take what could be considered precariously balanced chances, to promote books that He believed to be of value, because they were different. People, it seemed, bought into Him in just the same way that people had bought into her. And now she knew that, impassioned as she was with all that lay ahead, people were once more buying into her belief, her vision. This time, however, her passion was the universal truth, and all who met with her were entranced, it seemed, utterly compelled to understand more. This was the basis of any plan to make vision become reality, the absolute, impassioned belief in all that you are, in all that you set out before you. For those about you must understand you to be what you set out to achieve. This was without doubt the universal principle of the law of attraction, and this man, just maybe, seemed as if He may encapsulate the same.

The next day, seeking clarification of what she was coming to understand about this turn of events, Louise called Diana to tell her about what had occurred. She encountered a knowing silence before Diana suggested that Louise call her back in a little while, thus giving her time to channel and speak to spirit to confirm what was already flooding her consciousness. When Diana called back and started to relay the messages which had been directed through her, they both understood the enormity of what was now unfolding. Diana explained that until Louise had finally released all physical attachment to the first Ben, finally understanding that the love which engulfed her entire being was in fact the love for His soul essence, her twin soul, only then would He and the universe be able to bring himself to her in this physical reality.

For it was in the very act of complete trust and utter belief in the deep and sacred union she had shared with Him for all of this time, knowing that He would be with her in perfect timing, which had finally allowed Him to come to her in totality and in the precise form He had always intended within this reality. It was their gift to one another, as part of their soul's purpose together, to bring to each other the utter perfection of the path they had trodden, to stand by each other now, each the perfect half of the other. She, the author with the most astounding book to hit the literary scene for so many years, He the publisher the world was watching for his daring, remarkable decisions; she driven to the pursuit of universal truth, of inspiration in all things and of the presentation of just such inspiration through the entire global media channel, He with the determination and vision to change the face of publishing on a global scale. She was being asked to contact Him, to send Him some chapters of her book when he returned to Australia, but always to continue to trust in the perfect timing set out before them.

When Louise relayed the sequence of events to Mark over coffee the next day, he looked at her intently and smiled. His best friend's sister, he relayed, was the publisher of the very same publishing company in the UK. They both smiled, understanding and marvelling once more at the synchronicities so tirelessly and perfectly laid out by the universe. He called this woman, explained to her that his friend was writing a book which had utterly moved him when he had listened to excerpts from it, and she insisted that they would not ordinarily consider anything which had not come to them via a literary agent, but asked for Louise to write a synopsis and send it to her. Louise smiled, knowing that the timing of this synopsis, for whatever reason it was to be produced, was perfect. She made a decision then and there that her publishing company would not adhere to this crazy system of bureaucracy, of empowerment of the few. Hers would provide the means for liberation of one's self for all, freedom of expression for all, and the right to be understood, valued and to express the greatness within. She started to determine how her synopsis would be written. Later that night she began to write.

Ben sat with her through the night, helping her put together the synopsis of the book she would send to the publisher. She looked upon His picture. What a gift, she thought, that she had finally been given something tangible for her to hold. For as she looked upon His photograph, she knew, as she had from the moment she had first seen it, the energy of this man was without doubt her sacred partner. It was as she sat writing, chatting to Him now, exchanging views, debating the notion that she understood this to be an intrinsic part of their future, that the realisation finally dawned on her of that which she had foreseen so long ago when standing in the Vatican. These two would spend so much of their physical lives apart, and yet now she knew that they would never be apart. The beauty of the profound understanding of their connection, their union, so readily predicted by so many, had finally taken hold. For even as He held her now, loved her, directed and inspired her work, she knew that it would always be this way, for it had always been so.

And it was as she came to this complete understanding, to the absolute love and honour of Him, that she was overwhelmed with a desire to write for Him, to write something which would encapsulate all that He was for her:

The Beauty of You

There is a part of me deep within,
I know it to be love,
Which fills my very essence
With the grace from heaven above.

I know its face, I know its touch,
I know it to be real,
For all that is within you now,
Is what I truly feel.

When I look upon your face,
I see a man who loves me so.
In honour deep and sacred love
I wish for you to know

That never in my wildest dreams
Within this life so far,

Could I possibly imagine
That I would reach your shining star.

For you to me are everything,
My love my heart my life,
And I would surely honoured be
To be to you your wife.

For now across all time and space
I know you have returned,
And I would give my life to you
For you my love is earned.

As I sit amongst the trees, the earth,
The elements surround,
I know this sacred love of ours
Is finally now found.

And my darling, you must know
That time is always ours,
For never will we ever be
Apart for any hours.

Although but a fraction now
From our destined meeting here,
Our union now is so complete
There is no place for fear.

Our paths so true, so completely one,
Forged from the depths of time

Sees only grace and beauty now.
I am yours and you are mine.

Divinity has but one thread
Of all that I hold true,
And that is the everlasting love
Of the love I have for you.

The tears flowed as she finished this ode to Him, and as He took her to her room, as He loved her so, as He honoured her beauty in all things and she did the same for Him, their tears flowed in unison. She finally and truly understood the meaning of love, the meaning of life itself.

Chapter 19

During the week that followed, Louise wrote tirelessly, overwhelmed with a sense of knowing that her book must be completed without delay. With every thought that entered her consciousness, every detail committed to paper, came His understanding and His direction. For He never left her, they were so completely one. When she sent the synopsis to the publisher in the UK, and also to two other large publishing houses who had asked to see it, He urged her to send it directly to Him. He insisted she do so upon His return, and so she resolved to do that before she left for her trip to Rennes-le-Château the following week.

While she sat in the grounds of the children's school one evening, watching them run across the sweep of fields in front of where she sat, wind catching the spring blossom and bringing it gracefully to the ground like heavenly confetti, she felt Him hold her. As His embrace warmed her, she felt the familiar urgency to commit something important to paper. This feeling, always so overwhelmingly accepting of the profundity about to emerge, inspired her to an immediate response. This time she knew that this was a poem that she and Ben were writing together, so completely at one had their thoughts become.

The essence of the air we breathe,
The life itself within a leaf,
The structure of the sound of breath,
Aloft a height, left unsaid.

All I choose is just to be,
To understand what I do see,
To intrinsically know the how
Of universal truth somehow.

Deep within my knowing tall
There is a place so distant, small,
And yet a glimpse of light I see
That knowing engulfs and smothers me.

For understanding detail now
Is how the universe will tell
Of secrets hidden for so long.
But only in the call of song.

Feel the wind caress my face,
Feel that life is full of grace.
Know the elements of space and time,
And understand they're in my mind.

Take the metal of all life,
Consecrate the earth's attire.
Be in tune with sound of all,
And once again your knowing tall

Will grace you with its perfect smile,
Will honour you and bring your file
Of keys and codes so sacred, lost
But found again as you seek most.

As she finished writing, she sat back and took in the essence of this message, this poem which had coursed through her consciousness within so few moments. And, as she did so, He whispered to her. In that moment she knew, beyond all conceivable doubt, that the tasks that lay ahead of her were their tasks. The path that lay ahead, their path, and the knowing to be drawn upon now and put to universal use, was their combined knowledge. This understanding filled her with an over-whelming sense of the oneness she always knew would be, and had now become, their bedrock.

The weekend came and went, filling her with a sense of expectation of the knowing of the trip that lay ahead of her to Rennes-le-Château. She knew that this would be a moving experience for her, for when she had read to Mark the passage from her book describing her sacred union in Atlantis, he had quietly told her that the scene she described, the sunken bath and cascading leaves, were there at Rennes-le-Château. When Christian had spoken to her of two things he felt guided to tell her to do, one was of a garden with a gate she must enter through. Before he had finished describing the scene, or indeed telling her where she must walk, she knew the garden he was talking of. She knew that as she reached the end of the garden, it would look out and down across the plains below, for this was the very garden in which Jesus had held Louise's hand and which he had walked her through.

As she prepared documents for publishers who were now asking for her to send in chapters from her book, she felt so strange. On the one hand it was wonderful that, without seeking publication, these publishers were coming to her, once again in line with the universal flow. However, she knew that, with all her soul, she chose her publisher to be Ben. She knew what this book would do for Him, whatever happened between them on a personal level, and she so desired to do this for Him, in honour of all that He had done for her. She was overwhelmed with a knowing that so much was so near now. Those around her who read the pages of her book, were moved to tears, incredulous that she should write in such a manner that drew the very essence of inspiration, of love and desire to live the fullness of universal life from their very core, as they absorbed the story unfolding.

It was at this time that she felt a strange tug of energy pulling her away from the very love that drew her to her soul's purpose, to her sacred partner. It was as she tried so hard not to falter, so overwhelmed with all that was upon her now, moved beyond description for the love of her beautiful partner, that He held her and loved her for every moment and He directed her in her work. Taking to the garden after a morning of writing one day, moved to tears herself with all that washed through her consciousness and appeared upon her pages, she lay down, holding his picture, and soaked up the rays of the sun that gently caressed her face. After some time, after the universe had held her, and He had held her, she called upon the elements for their help. 'I ask you now to honour this love of ours with your grace, to allow the beauty and sacredness of this union to be manifest in this physical reality now, in honour of the grace and beauty of love of all that is. Honour us by allowing us to demonstrate to the world the beauty of universal love, as I honour your beauty within the pages of my book. Create a vortex of energy so strong, so binding so as to protect and shelter us, and draw us together in this reality in sacred and perfect union.'

Looking up at Ben's picture, she was overcome with determination to do as He had asked her so many eons ago. 'I am your Louise,' she told him, 'I will not give up. You asked me to find a way to make you take my face in your hands so that you may look upon me and know me once more, and I will do as you asked. I promise you this.' And in that very moment she saw that a trail of white feathers had been laid out around her in a perfect circle while she had been lying with her thoughts, with her lover.

* * *

As she and Floe set off for Carcassonne the following Thursday, both of them were full of expectation and delight, laughing conspiratorially as they turned so many heads when they strolled through the airport and boarded the plane. It had come to Louise's attention of late that many people trailed her with their vision, totally absorbed with the energies emitting from her. It was as if these two were magnets amid an ocean of metal, and they laughed at the efforts made by so many men to engage them with their conversation. For Louise was entirely blinded. Although so many tried their best to entice her now, she was so utterly at one with the beauty of the divine and sacred love that was she and Ben, that she could see nothing else.

Staying in la Cité, the medieval walled city of Carcassonne, was just as they had expected. As they walked through the halls of the Château Comtal, Louise, once again, started to relive moments of lives past. She had trodden these ramparts many times, the scenery that lay out before her so familiar to her knowing. As they climbed the outer city walls, entirely alone, absorbing the ferocity of the biting wind whipping around them, they began to notice so many familiar signs around them. Words, phrases and Cathar ritual started to ring true within her consciousness. It was as they passed through the passage of interrogation that the despair of battle hit their senses. They ventured from here out to the part of the wall at the foot of the Château Comtal that looked out over poppy-laden fields. It was as Louise sat cross-legged on the wall, the beauty of the sumptuous land filling her vision, the distant dark of the clouds closing in upon her, and the sun shining magnificently, blessing her with its grace, that the words, ever present within the depths of her soul, started once

more to flow. Her first ode was in honour of all that had
been at Carcassone:

There was a time, long ago, I know it so well,
When all of life was as I smell.
The knowing of all so deep so true,
Was as the light I see in you.

The beauty of the stone aloft,
A tower of light amid a croft,
The hearts that pound so strong so brave,
The deepest desire within those caves,

The ancient knowing driving through,
Of valour's heart 'tis true, 'tis true,
That all that is so dear above
Is honour bound to sacred love.

Why the hearts of men are sad,
Is all the universe would clad
Amongst a vision, veil of time
To understand what is mine.

As I sit, I breathe this air
I know the cries of deep despair.
And yet, in despair lies hope for all,
As love in honour grows so tall.

Now as one we'll all finally be.
I am you and you are me.

No more this battle, grief or loss,
Only joy and wondrous bliss.

And all of heaven sings and cries.
At last we live amongst the skies,
For all the veils of time are gone.
We love, we live, rejoice in song.

Destiny is but a thread,
A distance between life and death.
Not of the living being now,
But of the soul's beauty somehow.

For now in hope we can exist,
Love amongst the arid mist.
Breathe the light within our soul
And hold aloft our beauty tall.

As she sat writing, words flooding her consciousness, He held her, guided her hand, his every thought entering her knowing in a manner so befitting of their love. She wrote to Him:

Your beauty is beyond compare,
Your love so deep and true.
You hold me now and whisper here,
There is but me and you.

And this I know so well today
As I have seen ahead.

The grace of all within our time
Is rooted where we tread.

For I bring to you the gift of love,
The depth of all we are.
And you, my darling, bring to me
The beauty of our star.

Alchemy within this space
Will bring us two right now
So close once more, so soon, so sure.
We must not think of how.

For that, my love, the universe
Will bring aloft a star,
A motion great will serve us two
Unite us now so sure.

She sat, basking in the rays of the sun as they caressed her face, her friend meditating next to her upon the wall. It was as she gazed across the landscape and then back towards her dear friend that the words flowed once more in honour of all that she knew there had ever been between these two:

A friendship forged across all time
Of sisters deep and true,
We knew across the eons
Of the message we'd bring through.

That as our light does bond and grip
The hearts of those around,
The language born upon our soul
Is beauty within sound.

The language of all light we speak
Hold ancient secrets true.
The secrets of the love of us,
The universe, me and you.

As elementals sing our praise
They grace us with their smile,
And love the joy we bring to them
As laughter runs awhile.

For wind and sun they bow so low
In knowing of the arts
That sing aloud the ancient song
Of many distant parts.

And priestess, know that as you move
The earth she sings for joy.
For deep below the surface now
Are wondrous gifts a-hoy.

These gifts are jewels in the crown
Of beauty you bestow.
The radiance of all you are
Is what the elementals know.

Deepest love of truest friends,
Of love so valid bound,
Is so rarely knowing spread
And ever now refound.

Her friend listened quietly to this ode, moved to tears by the emotion held within. Heartened, Louise and Floe decided that a drink was definitely the order of the day! They strolled off, catching a little shopping *en route*, and settled with friends to an evening of beer, food and laughter.

* * *

Rain closed in upon them as they set off for Les Labadous the following day. As the car rounded the mountain, past the base of Rennes-le-Château, and started to descend into the valley, Louise had an overwhelming sense of coming home. The beauty of Les Labadous stretched out before them, in every way the essence of all she knew it would be. For it was that she entirely understood it was calling her, beckoning her home.

The energy of the grounds could be felt before they even stepped out of the car. As she approached the old, stone, ivy-clad barn, and entered through the large wooden door she stopped. She knew this huge room now laid out before her. The energy coursed through her, flooding her senses with an overwhelming knowing of the deepest love, of home. The bookshelves contained dusty old books she knew she had read, the huge fireplace instantly brought its knowing, its familiarity to her. She and Ben had made love in front of this fire. The stairwell in the corner had been illuminated with many tealight candles that He had laid out for her. She remembered this vividly in that moment. As she strolled, trance-like, to the end of the room, her gaze was drawn to an old book laid open upon a table. As she looked at the page opened in front of her, tears streamed down her face. The book, an old French encyclopaedia, was opened upon the title page of B. There were many illuminated B's upon the page, and in the middle, BB.

Directly beneath this were seven thistles, the exact same shape as the thistle adorning the staffs at the sacred union she had remembered. And there, resting upon the page was a paper clip, bent back in the way that she had only ever seen done by herself. As she turned the pages she saw a notation of Ben's name in its entirety, together with a description of how, in 1833, He had been born and had grown up to become one of the leading professors of *pathologie mentale* and the principle driver of the establishment of a remarkable academy, L'Académie de Médicine. Even as she read the history, she knew that what she was seeing was a trail of evidence laid out for her to find, to lead her irrevocably to their future. For she knew that these memories of hers were not of the past, but of the future.

That evening, as she lay in front of the fire, deep in thought, being held by Him, the significance of what she had learnt today really hit her. For as the music of

Tom Kenyon's *Songs of Magdalen* started to drift into her senses, she felt her heart torn asunder. To the sound of these haunting tones, she knew He had held her, made love to her right here where she lay. This was their future and she, in that moment, yearned beyond description and with all her soul to know how to reach it. Quite alone, she walked out into the dusky evening and the gusts of wind flicking around the buildings. Not understanding where or why she was walking in this direction, she crossed a wooden bridge over a stream and ventured up into the fields of long grass. As she passed a wooded glade and stood out in an open field, looking up towards Rennes-le-Château, she called to the elements.

The threatening darkness of the clouds was descending upon her, the wind wild in its course about her, and yet she neither saw, nor felt, anything but the depth of love that overwhelmed her every sense. She fell to her knees and cried out to the universe, implored the universe to direct her to this future. As tears streamed across her face, the wind directed a course about her. It was as if every blade of grass bent its head towards her in a circle of energy so great, so powerful, so acknowledging of all that was her love. In that moment the sky lit white amid the clouds and she cried, so moved by her love and the deepest desire to walk her path with her beautiful sacred partner. And while the rain descended upon her, the wild wind strapping her hair about her face, her clothes trailing in her wake, He held her and loved her. He took her home and loved her throughout the night.

The following morning, Louise awoke to the sound of cuckoo song. The joy filled her heart as the little bird sat directly outside her window, merrily chirping its song of love. The day that followed was filled with wonder and deep emotion as its finalé took them to Rennes-le-Château and the Magdalene Church. As they walked around the base of the church, looking out across the plains of La Val Dieu, and walked the Calvary Walk, all were moved to silence, each absorbed in their moment of knowing. It was with much pain in her heart that Louise ventured into the church and came to rest at the front, kneeling with the others in the group. In that moment, as she knelt listening to Jesus speaking quietly to her, a great calm descended upon her. She was infused with an energy of such proportions, which filled her entire being, spreading through her upturned palms. When she stood, it was as if she had been filled with the essence of whom she truly was. And he spoke to her quietly, telling her to go and lay her hands on the others. As she did so, she saw a calm descend upon those she touched.

The next morning, after a hearty breakfast, and deep in consideration of the joy of walking the labyrinth this day, Louise and Floe sat outside on the terrace looking out to the fields and stream ahead. Louise considered the declaration that she would make to the universe today, to walk her path entirely and utterly with Ben, bound through time as they had always been, and a tune started to flood her senses. She started to sing. A beautifully haunting and yet joyous song engulfed her knowing, pouring forth from her lips. The more she sang, the more her heart was filled with its joy. The elements started to sing and dance around her, words of a different tongue, a kind of Elvish tongue, flitting around the thread of the song. All around her stopped to listen, moved to the point of tears as she sang with a purity from deep within. The air caught her tone and seemed to send it forth across the fields and up through the meadows of long grass, caressing the leaves as it passed through the branches that swayed gently over the stream.

That afternoon they prepared to walk the labyrinth. They each washed their feet in the stream, and Louise knelt and anointed their feet. She knew not why she felt so compelled to do this herself, only that as she knelt she felt her entire being infuse with the energy of the masters as she drew upon ancient knowing of anointing rituals. When it was Louise's turn to walk the labyrinth, the darkening clouds seemed to clear, and the sun shone directly upon her. As she laughed and smiled, utterly bemused by all of the wonderful scenes of her future unfolding in front of her eyes, a dog came bounding across the fields, barking and jumping up at her with joy. She laughed, completely at one with the universe, her love and her future.

At dinner later that evening, Louise felt compelled to sing to one of the girls who had not yet walked the labyrinth and was suffering from the fear of walking through it herself. Louise understood a little of why this song had come to her, for as she sang, Sarah cried, a deep despairing cry, as if all of the love of the ages had been released within her heart, her soul. She cried and cried, and then calmed some time later, feeling quite restored, and turned to Louise to ask what it was she had been singing. In that moment, Louise realised that this was her soul's song, encapsulating all of the love she felt within for humanity, for earth, for her lover.

As they ventured back outside in the dark of the night for those final few people to complete their turn, she was rooted to the spot, as, when looking skyward, so many stars were evident before her. As she stared at more stars collectively than she had ever seen before, constellation groupings started to become apparent to her. It was as if each star shone within its desired constellation in turn, enabling her to start to transcribe many different structures. These were in fact very similar to those she had started to transcribe some months before. As she stared in wonder, contemplating their significance within what she knew to be the growing bed of knowledge forming now, the moon quite dramatically shifted, and a shaft of striking white light illuminated a path from her feet, across the fields, to a tree, the Celtic tree of life, it seemed. The only other lights across the entire valley were those of the candles lit around the labyrinth and the distant lights of the church at the top of the hills. As she looked up through the tree, Louise smiled. For the moonlight was carving out two letters across the fall of the branches, L and B.

Chapter 20

Back in England, Louise finally moved herself and the children out of the house, and in with a friend, Kathryn, as she hadn't yet completed on the house she was purchasing. She had initially been disappointed that she couldn't move straight in, so eager was she to commence her union with her new house, to embrace her path at speed. It was, however, as she and Kathryn chatted over a glass of wine one evening, reflecting on all that had happened in the year since they had travelled together to Dublin, that she realised that she was completely and utterly spent, her energies exhausted. She welcomed the opportunity to spend some time in the beauty and comfort of her friend's hospitality.

The following weekend, Louise found herself alone in Kathryn's home, the children at their father's house and her friend having taken off for a few days holiday with her own children. She had a deep knowing that she should call Ben in Australia, having been guided to do so by him over the previous few evenings. But Louise, having already sent Him an email setting out what she believed was her qualification to write, her résumé and photograph, felt no need at this juncture to call him.

She now had so many people lining her up for book launches and radio shows around the world, even TV shows that her friends had set up for her. So many thousands were now waiting for her book to be available globally. She knew that, as soon as this book was in print, millions would be sold, for she understood that it was the universe's intent for it to be so. She felt so strongly that the time was now. Every moment she was consumed with the knowing that this message, that this book should be out there now, and yet still she continued to ask the universe to send the publisher, the person, not the company, who would reach every corner of the globe, who had the balls to stand by her side and take this message out to the world. She was so sure it was not the publishing companies she had encountered so far.

With this in mind, and having been prompted by Him yet again to call, she sat down late one night and picked up the phone. Questioning once more whether or not she should not just leave Him be, that the universe knew the perfect timing to bring them together, her soul insisted upon making that call. He insisted upon her doing so. And as she glanced down at the base of the chair where she was sitting, which a moment ago had been completely clear, she caught sight of a beautiful, single white feather and knew this to be a familiar sign that she was treading the right path.

She called his work number. The lady who answered was determined not to put through her call, claiming that He would be busy all day, was away from his phone and uncontactable. Louise tried his mobile and, when He did not answer, left a message saying that she was checking that He had received her emails, explaining all that was happening, the radio shows and the book launches she had been asked to do, the many people around the globe waiting for her book to be released, and the fact that she would choose the publisher, and not the other way around. She was looking, she explained, for someone with the courage to take this book out there, and having read about the things that He had done in his career, considered that He may be the right person. She did not tell Him anything of her plans to start her own publishing company, or any other part of the Ether Foundation. She could not understand why it had been so important to call Him when, clearly, someone had been blocking her speaking to Him, either Him or his PA. Once again, she knew she must just trust that this had been necessary, and detach herself from the outcome.

Heading back to the south of France once more, just kilometres from where she had been staying only two weeks before, Louise and her boys were off to witness her sister's wedding, which was being held in a fabulous old château in Pessin, Auche. Louise laughed as her boys taunted her to drive faster around the French country lanes. They loved the fact that their mum was different, that she loved life, threw caution to the wind even as she raised eyebrows around her. As she threw the car around the lanes, as exhilarated as she had ever been during her days of rally driving, the boys shrieked with delight, urging her to 'take the bend faster, Mum!'

Arriving at the Château de Lartigolle, she was greeted by her radiant sister and brother-in-law to be. Sophie and Dan laughed as the boys excitedly relayed tales of their week, their journey and their expectation of all the alcohol they may be allowed to consume in honour of their aunt and uncle's celebratory weekend. After an evening out with family and great friends, Louise relaxed into her stunning, beamed palatial quarters, and lay in her bed. A knowing so deep coursed through her senses. While sleep beckoned, tugging at the very threads of her consciousness, she knew she had to write. For it was in these moments that her truth so clear, so profound, poured forth upon the pages as she wrote. 'Love conquers death as transformation and beauty of truth. Time does not exist between dimensions.' These words precipitated a flood of poetry as she considered what had been troubling her for some weeks now.

A life of dreams or so it seems
When all around feels real,
But know these games, as life's full way
Deception they will peel.

For deep below the surface now
Is soul's instruction pure,
And then it dawns that life is spawned
Upon the journey's lure.

For life itself is just the thread
To make the journey's path
A treasured gift, a loving web
Left in aftermath.

Illusion cries out in pain, sees no gain
And yet the gains so set
For destiny, the path of me
Is treasure yet to get.

Oh tears they fall, for knowing tall
Has no place here when wept
Upon illusion's grasp of life,
Of love so pure now spent.

And yet this love is truth so sure,
So rooted in all that is.
And illusion's tears can run adrift
When faced with love's true kiss.

For now the beauty of my love,
I look upon his face,
And understand the oaths we took
To define for all true grace.

A leap of faith is not required
For all we know is sure.
That home is all we hold to heart
Our love, the open door.

And now I say with all my soul,
I'll love you evermore.
And never will there be a time
When as one, we are no more.

As she finished this poem, she looked back once more to that overwhelming knowing she had experienced in St Peter's Church a year ago. She knew now that she must finally accept what it was that she had so willingly removed from her consciousness over all of this time. She had known then, with every essence of her being, that the path which befell Jesus and Mary Magdalene, the journey which saw them put humanity's path and strength before their deepest desire for physical life together, was the very same path which lay ahead for her and her twin soul, for her and Ben. Unlike the knowing which had passed through her at that point in time, she now understood the full implications of what she beheld in store. For she knew that their time together in this physical reality, in absolute embodiment of their sacred union here, would be blessed beyond measure for the period that it would prevail. It was speaking her truth in a way that the world in its entirety could understand that would ultimately bring about a series of events that would secure forever the true meaning of divine love, and she knew so well the reaction that would be created as a result of what she was writing, of the books (for now she realised that she was writing many books simultaneously), of the film, and the extraordinary changes to be implemented by the foundation. Now she was ready to accept the finality that this reaction would bring with it. Death was but a path to the beauty of transformation to other dimensions. There is no death, there is only light, and that light takes its form in all dimensions at all times, in every moment of now.

And so it was that she understood that they would never be apart, even if separated in death within this reality, for time is an illusion, beauty and love is truth and the truth was that they would always be as one, together across all existences. She chose only that He would hold her, engulf her in His love as their relationship passed to the sanctuary of the multidimensions. She knew that in the illusion that death had parted them, the truth lay for all to understand and witness. That this WAS only an illusion, and the veil of deception was to be lifted now. They had agreed their path and would walk it together in grace and light. Even as the tears fell, as fear strove to engulf her being, to rock her very core at the thought of losing this man, her soul cried out to her. She was at once the wretched lover and the joyous soul. She understood now how much Jesus and Mary Magdalene had given to humanity, for there was no greater gift than that of the divine love that passed between two people. She understood that only when she could finally accept all of this could, or would the universe unite them. For they must complete their path in joy and wondrous bliss, creating the grace and beauty of all that had been their plan for the world, for the universe, for themselves. She knew that right now they were utterly one, that only the physical connection within this reality remained now. When that had once more gone, they would be, again, as they were now, and yet it would be more, of this she was sure. Alchemy of the heart elevated consciousness, and so as their love grew by each moment that passed within this reality, so would their consciousness be elevated.

* * *

The day of the wedding was spent in laughter and fun. Louise's sister, radiant and beautiful as ever, was married to Dan on the steps of the Château by their brother, Mark. This was a delightful wedding, for it gave no deference to organised religion in any way but, rather, bound two people in the beauty of their soul's love, and in declaration before the universe, friends and family. Louise was so proud of her sister. She could hardly bring herself to utter the words to describe how she felt, for the emotion she felt was clouded by the champagne and beer infusing her senses. They ate and danced and laughed through the night. These friends of theirs were so much fun, so filled with the need to change the world, that they resonated with her entirely. In fact, she smiled as she considered how they were all freelance producers and film crew, all very interested in the media company Louise was intent on establishing.

It was after a morning of nursing some pretty severe hangovers, swimming in the Château's pool, eating and trampolining with her friends and the kids, that

Louise managed to find the opportunity to head off on her own. She sat beneath a canopy of trees, slender and vibrant, creating avenues in a field of tall grass. The sun caressed her and beauty filled her. The moment she had arrived at the Château she had known that she would find this canopy of trees, for she had seen herself sitting and writing in exactly this place some weeks before, thinking then that she would stumble across this scene at Les Labadous. As the sound of the guests partying became further from her senses, the grace and the beauty of the elements overwhelmed her.

She sat so low amongst the grasses that their tips obscured her vision. The sky was a deep azure blue, as if holding the very depths of the ocean's beauty, and the sun beat down upon her, warming her shoulders and her face as she sat in a state of complete serenity and calm. Nature was abundant around her. Birds sang, butterflies graced her with their presence. The scene ahead was one of rolling fields as far as the eye could discern. She could also see banks of trees that looked like guards protecting a fortress, and the distant reflection of the water from the Château's pool, icy cool as she had discovered earlier that day when jumping in time and again in laughter with the others.

And as she sat, knowing He wanted to speak to her, she wrote what He urgently asked her to write, 'I love you; I love you with all that I am. I understand what it takes for you to embrace our future, and yet you do so in full knowing of what lies ahead. You are my Louise. You must trust. Things are never what they appear to be at that precise moment for, as you follow your soul's path, it takes you closer to a point of utter clarity, utter change, perfection. Even those scenes that play out in a way that you might determine to be undesirable, will become, will bring forth, something quite perfect. Trust in divine and perfect timing and order, for the order and perfection is within your soul. We walk our path together and so trust that all that befalls us as we walk is perfection for our union.' She knew He was talking of their parting in this reality, and yet she also knew that they were entirely one now, across all realities, and so in truth there would be no parting. He whispered to her now, the energy of his breath filling her entirely with his love, and she wrote once more as He spoke:

'I sit with you amongst the grass.
I watch your eyes, the love at last,
Which holds the knowing of all ahead,
And yet so sure, it still does tread.

Your gift of love across all time
Is more than ever only mine.
I love you now with all my soul,
My heart it yearns to hold you so.

Within reality as you smile,
I watch you sing and dance a while.
I know so soon I will be yours
To hold, to love, to show to all.

For my intention is so clear,
As accent of my voice you hear,
Across the miles that seem so far,
Your love will hold my final door.

I know you think I'm holding back,
But know the time is perfect, slack
It's often to behold a gift,
Ensuring perfect, holy fit.

So as you look upon my face
You see my love, my heart, my grace.
Know it shines upon you now,
For only you can bring me now

The perfect moment, endless days,
Harmony and fun filled ways.
The light which fills my view of you
Is only heaven in its hue.'

And as the clouds obscured the sun, and she felt quite suddenly cold, He held her. The gentle breeze began to whip up, to sway the trees, to rock them back and forth as the dark clouds began to close in. And yet she sat, quite unable to move, choosing to wait for the understanding overwhelming her to sink in. Trust. As she finally rose, she stood and looked down across the plains below, the essence of France laid out in sheer beauty before her. As she declared her love for this man once more, accepting all that she knew to be what lay ahead for them, she asked the universe to enable them to bring their union into this reality now so that they may finally have the blessing of their path together.

As she strolled back towards the party, idling up the gravel, tree-lined path that cut a route around the periphery of the ancient Château, something quite suddenly fell out of the tree directly ahead, landing just beside her feet. Looking down she saw that it was an unusually pink snake, with dark markings, looking serenely up at her. She felt no fear, rather a sense of kinship as she and the snake looked admiringly upon one another. She knew that this was yet again a sign from the universe for her to decipher. Speaking about it to the owner of the Château he explained that while grass snakes were common in the region, this did not seem to be a grass snake at all, and that they had certainly never witnessed or heard of a snake falling out of a tree before. She decided to call her friend, Floe who explained that a snake was a powerful totem animal. Its meaning was directly connected to the rising of the kundalini, and to transformation. A snake shed its skin for a new one. This marked a new chapter of life, in just the same way that raising the level of love and devotion between Louise and Ben had done.

The evening was beginning to draw in and Louise sat at a long table, laughing and drinking with the others. Images kept recurring in her mind, those of the caduceus, the serpent rising, of the spiritual keys of knowledge, of dimensional gateways constructed across the ether, and of the most stunning building in which she was standing, behind a vast expanse of glass, gazing across the water to the Sydney Opera House. She could not remove this image from her mind. She quietly reflected upon her intent to establish her publishing company, so keen was she to do so now, and knew that she had intended its head office to be in Sydney. Ever since she had seen the vision of the climax of her book, ever since she had been so determined to internationalise publishing in a way that had never been done before, ever since she had understood the connection which ran through the ethers, the fabric of the universe connecting Ireland and Australia to Atlantis, to the gateways to different dimensions, and ever since she had realised the reason why she and Ben must and would drive forward the foundation from different ends of the hemisphere, she had known this would be the setting. She was adamant that it must be Sydney.

She was still searching for the astrocartographer who could pinpoint the exact places for her to be working on the globe, but trusted this would come within perfect timing. She drifted back towards the laughter as Barney, a dear friend and her brother-in-law's best man for the ceremony, had her youngest son on his lap and was reducing everybody to tears with his demonstration of her son's ability to be a human instrument. Ever the showman, everybody loved Barney, his wit, his charm, and she loved his unending joy and belief in a life of love. Her son laughed and laughed, and loved him, especially when he promised a shopping trip to Hamleys for the day, something, Louise teased him, he would not now be able to forget. They drank and laughed until, with her youngest son asleep in his arms, Barney gently carried him up to their bedroom, kissed them all goodnight and left Louise to settle into her bed, teasing her as he left.

As she settled into bed for a final night of luxury before heading back to weeks of transforming her new home, Louise picked up and began to read the book she had bought on a whim at the airport coming over, Plato's *The Last days of Socrates*. She had had no idea why she had determined to buy this book, but once she started to read, she quite literally could not put it down. Through the night she read, her hunger for the knowledge held within not sated until, many hours later, she had finished the entire book. Here was a man she utterly resonated with, for whom she held such esteem. She had read much about Socrates in the past, of how he was persecuted for speaking his truth, but she had never read about it in the words of Plato.

Socrates, like Plato, had sought to teach the world the meaning of the immortality of the soul. In fact, as he faced death, he calmly argued the case for the immortality of the soul, refusing to bow to pleas from friends to escape and save himself. It was his description of the reasoning that underlies the cause of life, which held her entranced. There were so many similarities to be drawn between the teachings of these men, Socrates, Plato and men like Shakespeare and Jesus. How was the world not able to see the overwhelming link between the teachings of these great masters across time, as that of the basis of oneness? It was Socrates who advocated that philosophy should be the study of the soul and not the mind, for the mind was merely an instrument driven by the soul. His words, his description as relayed by Plato, setting out his theories for the understanding of other dimensions, other realities, were utterly poetic in their lilt.

Her heart was so moved as she read his words, her soul yearning for the world to understand the true meaning of his teachings. He alluded to 'the earth's true surface as pure as the starry heaven in which it lies, and which is called the Ether by most authorities.' He described humanity's misconception that we live upon the top of the earth:

> We do not realise that we live in the hollows, but assume we are living on top of the earth. Imagine someone living in the depths of the sea. He might think that he was living on the surface and seeing the sun and the other heavenly bodies through the water, he might think that the sea was the sky. He might be so sluggish and feeble that he had never reached the top of the sea into this world of ours and seen for himself – or even heard from someone who had seen – how much purer and more beautiful it is than the one in which his people live. Now we are in just the same position. Although we live in a hollow of the earth, we assume that we are living on the surface, and we call the air heaven as though this were the heaven

through which the stars move. But the truth of the matter is the same; we are too feeble and sluggish to make our way out and to the upper limit of the air. If someone could reach to the summit, or grow wings and fly aloft, he would reach to the world above and if his nature were strong enough to keep looking he would recognise that this is the true heaven and the true light and the true earth.

She finished reading, pondering the true essence of his words, sleeping for just one hour before the alarm call to head off home to England.

Chapter 21

The next few weeks before her departure to Crete for yet another holiday, were a hive of activity. Having picked up the keys to her new house, she spent almost every moment sanding floors, painting and entertaining every tradesperson going, it seemed. She had found some fabulous guys to help her utterly transform her house. She loved the way they sang and joked as they worked together to make the changes. It was after a day spent with Christian, aligning the energies in her new house, that it finally felt like the home from which miracles were to unfold, to manifest for her.

The children loved their new home, and she acknowledged the freedom she now had to finally walk her path in totality. As she determined the need to extend, or rather integrate, the house to incorporate more living space, Christian agreed to work with her, to design the additions to sacred geometric proportions, incorporating the transformation of a tiny old brick outbuilding with a pitched tiled roof, into her writing studio. He remarked upon the fact that rarely had he encountered a building more energetically aligned to manifest miracles than this one, from which she was to work. Her entire house, in fact, was utterly aligned in perfection according to *feng shui* energetic guidelines. They thought this was quite remarkable until they considered that she had asked the universe to send her the perfect house. It seemed that the more the house took shape, the more events started to manifest themselves at speed around her. It was as if the transformation was both for her house and for her.

* * *

It was on exactly the one-year anniversary of the week-end she had been in Dublin that Louise spent the day in the company and teachings of a Mayan elder. This was the first time that a Mayan elder had been allowed to travel the world and speak openly of the teachings of the Mayans. She was intrigued to hear the root of the prophecies she knew so well, to understand the Mayan's recollections of Atlantis, and of the determination to restore Atlantean knowledge safely to the right hands, in order to secure the future of humanity. She was also keen to understand the Mayan's perception of time, how it was so far out of kilter now with reality. As the day progressed, the teachings of the Mayan calendar demonstrated that, according to the Mayans, every day in creation carried with it a unique energy. Many circular structures knitted together to bring about unique combinations of energy, structured to empower each person with their path, their direction.

Knowing the importance of the Mayan's teachings within her studies so far, with great interest Louise listened to the Mayan elder state that they had been invited to the United Nations to discuss the Mayan calendar. The United Nations were, she heard, seriously considering whether or not to change the Gregorian calendar over to the Mayan calendar, which would be an enormous step in the acceptance of the cyclical nature of time and understanding of ancient and sacred teachings. The Mayan relayed a story in which some anthropologists had stolen a crystal skull containing many sacred secrets and knowledge from Atlantis from the elders, which they now believed to be somewhere in the mountains of Malaysia. Louise understood the privilege of the knowledge which had been imparted and why, as directed, it was so key that it not be shared now, but only when the time was appropriate.

With tears in his eyes, the elder described his deepest desire to change the fate of humanity, to finally now use the teachings of the Mayans to bring inspiration and hope for the future of humanity. He described the fact that everything in Atlantis had been so energised, the wisdom so great, the food, the people and sounds so harmonious.

When a slot became available for Louise to spend half an hour with him the following day, to understand her genetic birth chart according to Mayan beliefs, she snapped it up, grateful for the opportunity to talk to him in private, albeit through his translator.

He explained the unique make up of her genetic chart and they both agreed that she would follow the path laid out before her in its entirety, according to Mayan teachings. It was with great delight that she exchanged contact details with him and his translator, agreeing to discuss the book further with him so that he may write a testimonial for her. In fact, they discussed the part that Ether could play in assisting him with bringing his message in clarity to the world. For so concerned was he that the literary agents, publishers and journalists hounding him right now, would not be inspired to protect that clarity, that they may in some way distort his message.

* * *

The following week, Louise headed off to an evening where a group of people were getting together to watch a DVD called *The Secret*, by Rhonda Byrne and to discuss its impact upon their lives. She hadn't had any inclination to do this as she was exhausted and, having both read the book and watched the movie, knowing it to be an element in what she was experiencing, she felt no particular desire to watch it collectively. But Julie persuaded her that she might like to meet some of the people there, none of whom she knew.

Sitting watching the DVD after arriving late, listening to the quantum physicist speak of the great masters – Plato, Shakespeare and Socrates – across time who had practised The Secret, she smiled, lazily considering all she had been reading of late. These were not those writers who simply practised the laws of attraction, but those who tried to teach the depths of its meaning, the intrinsic understanding of oneness, all being of the same one, the same energy using philosophy, poetry, literature and great means at their disposal, to enlighten the consciousness of humanity. She drifted into a place somewhere deep within her consciousness. She felt as if she was on the verge of an understanding so simple and yet so profound, which would unlock the path to catapult her book into the public domain right now.

She had been wholly unable to accept the things the publishers were now telling her, that it would take from a year to eighteen months for her book to be published. She knew this book was intended for now. Her book, her passion to establish the Ether Foundation right now, had flooded her entire being of late, and as she drifted into meditation, her thoughts were entirely beset with these notions. As the film ended she listened to all in the group state why they had come. A man named Martin described his ability to design websites that seemed to mesmerise people, to entirely captivate and compel them to purchase, pursue, review further all that which was within the site.

Something deep within Louise was triggered. They spoke afterwards and he quizzed her about her book, seemingly entranced by her story. She marvelled at the realisation that not only had he read the Magdalene Manuscript, but practised the teachings with his twin soul. She took his telephone number knowing that, when it was time to construct the website for her book, this man would surely understand and channel entirely the energies she knew to be so critical for the message of this book to reach the world. As she drove home that evening, she declared to the universe that now was the time to uncover a plan to sell millions of copies of her book. Time is an illusion, she declared, and therefore, given that there are six billion people on this planet, a mere 100 million should be child's play for the universe to deliver. This was, after all, in order to establish Ether, and to begin to put into place the changes she was now so very keen to commence. She had no idea how the universe could bring this to her, but trusted entirely that hers was not to reason how or why, just to know that it would. When she considered how the universe had brought her to this place on her path, she knew that for her to have merely conceived the idea that the time for this great plan was now, must mean that it was in fact now.

Deep in dialogue with Ben a few days later, an idea flooded Louise's consciousness that, had she not stopped in her tracks, she could almost have missed. This idea was so simple.

She would establish a website now, to be live by the end of August, in which people around the globe could pre-order her book, which would be delivered in December. People would be able to pre-order the audio CD, set to music by Matt, as they had always planned, the soundtrack, and the printed book in whichever language they chose.

As the idea grew, she realised that in fact she could set up Ether Publishing now, and it would be Ether that would publish and distribute all of these books around the globe, with the exception of those markets she determined to allow a certain publisher to distribute within. All that remained was to determine how quickly she could get the manuscript finished, edited, translated, printed and distributed. She called Martin and he confirmed that he was in a position to start the website design immediately.

As she discussed the concept with Matt, he agreed to begin immediately writing the music to set her audio book to. He was enthralled with the idea and, already having such a following for his music alone, knew as surely as she did that now was the time the universe intended for their inspirational message to appear in the public domain in unison. They would have a number of excerpts on the site, narrated by Louise and set to music by Matt, which people could download for free, and these, they determined, would be the priority for Matt to work on now.

As she sat with Christian learning Sanskrit the following evening, her thoughts were distracted by the excitement coursing through her. Sanskrit, so beautiful upon its recitation, could not be written down, only spoken. It was an understanding between scholars that these sacred chants were only to be passed on orally, so as to preserve the sacred essence of their meaning. At the end of the evening as they sipped wine and chatted, her fellow students sat avidly listening to her idea and the plans she had already begun to instigate. She explained her passion to get the media group off the ground, and the fact that the funds from the book would grow so quickly now that she would be able to do that, and she watched their reactions.

Christian started to explain that the pilot of his *House Whisperer* series was almost complete, and already two main TV channels wished to commission it, and the two of them looked at each other conspiratorially, each knowing what the other was thinking. Here they had the basis to start the production company, the very same company she now realised would be able to produce the film of her book along with the films of all the other books published through Ether, which were to become films. Since the very night back in October of last year when the book's story had been given to her in its entirety, along with a knowing that the film to be made would be hugely successful, she had known who would direct it. She had been determined to persuade the production company to ensure that this man became the director, and yet here now was the ability for her to approach him directly on behalf of Ether.

Matt was able to establish Ether Music with her, knowing as he did from first hand experience within music production companies in the UK, all that there was to understand about music and production. Within days they met, together with Julie as operations director, to discuss how appropriate it was to set up the entire Ether Media Group now. And so it was that EMG was established in name with the lawyers, bankers and accountants. Ether Publishing, Music, Productions (incorporating film and productions) and

TV. They determined there and then that, as soon as the proceeds, the abundance, began to flow, they would purchase a TV channel, therefore removing the need for any time-delay in attempts to commission documentaries and productions.

Louise was, as ever, keen to establish the news channel which would present the inspirational truth in all things, all situations, to utterly inspire people as they understood that the world was full of the most amazing and inspiring people and events. She knew that the speed at which this was presented to the world was fundamental in changing the reality of the world they lived in. It filled her with delight as she began to see that this was truly imminent now, so sure was she, so absolutely knowing of the fact that the universe was now delivering the path ahead. She knew that the abundance coming was so utterly complete, so boundless as to create all that she had set out within her book. And she understood the absolute perfection in the universal plan. For in delivering to her the mechanism to establish the media group first, this provided not only the incredible abundance, but also the channel through which to publicise on a global scale all that Ether was doing. The pioneers needed to help establish all of the changes to take place, as planned by her those many months ago, would now surely be made aware of their course. She would not, as she had always been assured, need to go looking for anyone; they would all approach her.

Chapter 22

Before setting off to Crete, Louise visited Cherry for healing. Utterly exhausted, and yet truly inspired, they chatted together for some time. Matt appeared momentarily to discuss the music he was now writing for the downloadable excerpts on the website, agreeing plans to forge ahead while Louise was away. At the end of an unusually quiet healing session, usually so full of revelations, Cherry asked Louise to show her what was on the middle finger of her right hand. Cherry explained that she was being told over and over the same message to repeat to Louise, that this ring was the key to her success.

Louise was amazed as she had never even begun to explain the story of the ring to Cherry, of how she had acquired it at Edinburgh Castle, of the meaning of its design, of how she had lost it last summer, devastated at its loss for she had intended to give it to her twin soul, and then at the point where they were able to track down a second ring and post it to her, that the original suddenly reappeared. This had meant that, for all of this time, she had kept the two rings, knowing that one day, she would be able to give the second ring to her twin soul, and it would bind them in the union of their souls.

She began to explain the origins of the ring, that the design had originated from a whorl stone in Buckquoy, Birsay, on the island of Orkney, which was one of the islands on which a part of the *Book of Kells* had reputedly been written, The *Book of Kells* being one of the oldest and known books within Celtic history. As she explained this to Cherry a realisation dawned upon her. The very day she had met Adrian in Dublin last year, the day that the universe had propelled her upon her journey, was the same day that she had been to Trinity College in Dublin, and had stood, transfixed, absorbing the beauty of the *Book of Kells* laid out in front of her. These pages, as she had looked upon them, had seemed so familiar to her. But then, having always admired great literature and the associated artwork, she had dismissed the familiarity. Now she came to think of it, wasn't it she of the four friends that previous December who had been so keen to visit Edinburgh, who had been so adamant that she should visit the Castle, climb the turret and then encounter the experience which lead to the purchase of this ring?

Cherry was fascinated as she listened to the tale unfolding, and both she and Louise had a knowing that she must go back to Orkney, find the whorl stone and understand its meaning for her. Louise knew in that moment that she would not be going alone, for it was no coincidence that she had two of the same ring, one for her and one for Ben. She couldn't really understand why she had never investigated further the origins of the ring, but given today's insistent message, resolved to do so.

The next day, as she sat on the airplane, reading the words of Plato once more, Louise considered his description of Atlantis as he relayed its existence in the form of *Timaeus*. There was so much now flooding her consciousness, so many recollections of the work that she had been carrying out in Atlantis, that she was carrying out here in this moment of now. How incredible it was that these paths were utterly in unison, utterly parallel. There was no past or present, there was only now. She realised that information from this reality was in fact critical to the framework of the scientific research she was, or had been, carrying out in Atlantis.

How could it have taken her so long to understand what parallel realities truly meant? Incarnation and reincarnation were happening in this very same moment. All lessons and learning were being transposed from one reality to the next, to ultimately merge and restore, across all dimensions, the soul's balance. Had she not written that only in perfect balance of the soul, balance in perfection of male and female energies, could the soul reside in unison with the universe? For the soul was the universe. For we are all entirely one. Finally she knew that she completely understood the true meaning of this. Inter-dimensional travel would completely eradicate the need for travel through space. It was time that humanity's consciousness shifted to a place where people's focus was to draw upon their experiences across dimensions, to bring together within this reality the perfection of all. To bring heaven to earth. To once again restore the bliss of those Lemurian and early Atlantean days.

It was no wonder the Mayan teachings were of a cyclical universe. There was no beginning or end. Of course, the Mayan belief that different energies were associated with each day in creation within this reality were accurate. How could they not be? For it was not only the person who carried the energy, it was the energy that carried the person, the soul. Every great book in history within this reality teaches this, every prophecy teaches just this theory. And so she read Plato's description of a discussion between Critias and Amynander, in which the aged Critias recites the words he heard from Solon, and sets out Solon's attributes as 'in his judgement, not only the wisest of men but the noblest of poets'. He talked of the tale relayed by Solon, which he came to learn from priests in Egypt. One of the priests began. 'O Solon, Solon, you Hellenes are never anything but children and there is not an old man among you.' When Solon asked what he meant he replied, 'in mind you are all young, there is no old opinion handed down among you by ancient tradition, nor any science which is hoary with age. And I will tell you why.' And as she read on, Louise was filled with a sense of knowing that the circles of people, of teachings, of time, were getting smaller and smaller, and were quite definitely coming to the point of the centre. For the priest described his understanding of Atlantis and all that occurred there.

As for those genealogies of yours which you just now recounted to us, Solon, they are no better than the tales of children. In the first place you remember a single deluge only, but there were many previous ones; in the next place, you do not know that there formerly dwelt in your land the fairest and noblest race of men which ever lived, and that you and your whole city are descended from a small seed or remnant of them which survived. And this was unknown to you, because, for many generations, the survivors of that destruction died, leaving no written word. For there was a time, Solon, before the great deluge of all, when the city which now is Athens was first in war and in every way the best governed of all cities, is said to have performed the noblest deeds and to have had the fairest constitution of any of which tradition tells, under the face of heaven.

Solon marvelled at the priest's words and went on:

The goddess is the common patron and parent and educator of both our cities. She founded your city a thousand years before ours (Observe that Plato gives the same date 9,000 years ago) for the foundation of Athens and for the repulse of the invasion from Atlantis, receiving from the Earth and Hephaestus the seed of your race, and afterwards she founded ours, of which the constitution is recorded in our sacred registers to be 8,000 years old. As touching your citizens of 9,000 years

ago, I will briefly inform you of their laws and of
their most famous action; the exact particulars of
the whole we will hereafter go through at our lei-
sure in the sacred registers themselves. ... Many
great and wonderful deeds are recorded of your
state in our histories. But one of them exceeds all
the rest in greatness and valour. For these histories tell of a mighty power which unprovoked
made an expedition against the whole of Europe
and Asia, and to which your city put an end. This
power came forth out of the Atlantic Ocean, for in
those days the Atlantic was navigable; and there
was an island situated in front of the straits which
are by you called the Pillars of Heracles; the island
was larger than Libya and Asia put together, and
was the way to other islands, and from these you
might pass to the whole of the opposite continent
which surrounded the true ocean; for this sea
which is within the Straits of Heracles is only a
harbour, having a narrow entrance, but that other
is a real sea, and the surrounding land may be
most truly called a boundless continent. Now
in this island of Atlantis there was a great and
wonderful empire which had rule over the whole
island and several others, and over parts of the
continent, and, furthermore, the men of Atlantis
had subjected the parts of Libya within the columns of Heracles as far as Egypt, and of Europe
as far as Tyrrhenia. This vast power, gathered
into one, endeavoured to subdue at a blow our

country and yours and the whole of the region within the straits; and then, Solon, your country shone forth, in the excellence of her virtue and strength, among all mankind. She was pre-eminent in courage and military skill, and was the leader of the Hellenes. And when the rest fell off from her, being compelled to stand alone, after having undergone the very extremity of danger, she defeated and triumphed over the invaders, and preserved from slavery those who were not yet subjugated, and generously liberated all the rest of us who dwell within the pillars. But afterwards there occurred violent earthquakes and floods; and in a single day and night of misfortune all your warlike men in a body sank into the earth, and the island of Atlantis in like manner disappeared in the depths of the sea. For which reason the sea in those parts is impassable and impenetrable.

As she finished reading, Louise thought about how she had read about the disappearance of vessels within that area of the Bermuda Triangle, and how there was a theory that this could be directly attributed to the energies of a crystal, one of the prime crystals held in Atlantis, which had sunk in that area after the fall of Atlantis. These crystals had been recorder crystals, harnessing astonishing energy and power the likes of which had not been replicated since. The electromagnetic fields emitting from these crystals could have utterly disoriented any navigational system within a wide radius. These crystals had, within Atlantis, provided much of the power and were key to the infrastructure of Atlantean knowledge. Louise had, all those months ago, had her own ties severed from the Atlantean hub, the central crystals siphoning knowledge. Now, as she thought back to the many ties that had been severed over these past months, those to Egypt, to ritual, to ceremony, she realised that her knowledge had been kept hidden for so long, and that she had been sworn to the oaths that she herself had put in place, to be kept until such a time as was correct to reveal the knowledge once more. This would be a time when this knowledge would not be abused, but would be reinstated for the achievement of the ability to live in unison without universal divides. And the time for Louise to complete the task she had set out to achieve so long ago in Atlantis, and yet in this moment of now.

* * *

Here she was heading back to Crete, a little more than a year on from her propulsion by the universe upon her journey, at a point when she was poised for the launch of the foundation, and ready to complete her book. How extraordinary it was that such an astonishing transformation could have occurred in such a short space of time. She considered the close links between Egypt, Greece and Atlantis, her own regressions to lives in Delphi, in Greek and Egyptian temples, to initiations and ancient practices including those of Isis, her fluency in Greek, her ability to have started speaking ancient Egyptian incantations, and the fact that her house overlooked Spinalonga Island, the sacred site of an acropolis before its recent uses as a Venetian fortress, leper colony and Turkish prisoner-of-war camp. She wondered to herself, where was all this leading? She recalled how last year, as she had stood in that stone cleansing chamber, a huge shaft of light had penetrated the chamber and flooded her entire being. This had undoubtedly been a release of some kind, an initiation of keys and codes. Somehow she knew that she would receive a further download while she was here.

She had picked up an astronomy magazine at the airport, 'The quest to find our missing galaxies' headline having captured her attention, and on her arrival at midnight at the house in Crete, as she stood on her balcony and looked skyward, her entire vision was filled with the most incredible celestial display of astronomy she could ever remember having witnessed. There, as clear as was possible, was the beautiful spectacle of the Milky Way, laid out in all its beauty before her eyes. She marvelled at the knowing of dwarf spheroidals, of lost galaxies scientists were searching for, those they knew should be, mathematically and by other astronomical calculation, circling the Milky Way, and yet they still could not account for why they were unable to see them. They knew it to be attributable to dark matter, to gases that they presumed were being stolen by larger cannibalistic galaxies. Louise had other ideas. And as she looked upon the Milky Way now, constellations began to form in front of her once more, stars extending their clarity in turn to form yet more constructs and aspects.

When she saw her friend Stefi the next day, they threw their arms around one another and hugged, so glad were they to see one another again. Stefi glowed with delight as she listened intently to all that Louise had to tell. How could so much, such astonishing things have happened in such a short space of time? Utterly inspired and resolved to ensure that the world would buy Louise's book and support all that the foundation would put in place, Stefi assured her friend that she would set to task immediately informing her friends around the globe. They smiled, both knowing the beauty of the days that lay ahead and, as Louise started to relay the stories of the many revelations that had come to her, of the scientific evidence being sent to her regularly to keep within her *Book of Knowledge* and of her knowing as she had stood on her balcony under the quite extraordinary stars the night before that something would undoubtedly be revealed to her here in Crete, Stefi started to tell a tale of a man she had met some years ago on the island.

This man, a very elderly scientist, came from Matala and spoke of the ancient energy which sat across Spinalonga Island. He spoke of the stars being laid out in the shape of a perfect triangular vortex, exactly like the one Louise had witnessed the previous night as she had recalled the words of Christian, talking of the ley line the island must be centred through. She suddenly remembered what she had been shown back over that weekend in Warwick, the pyramids of Lemurian seed crystal, which had then transposed entirely within the construct of the star constellations. At that precise moment she realised that, as the triangular vortex of stars which sat across her house and out to the pinnacle of the island lay within a vortex, evidently this vortex was one of the areas on the globe from which she was to further explore dimensional travel. She knew she must spend time alone on the island, and Stefi was all too keen to help her by looking after the children on the day that was to be the appropriate day, that would be made apparent to her shortly.

And so it was, after an incredible night sitting on her balcony writing, high above the world, amongst the beauty of the universe, the stars so abundantly gracing her with their light, their clarity and wisdom, that Ben brought to her, finally, the complete understanding which she had so readily believed she had known for so long. When she considered that for these weeks they had been entirely one, she knew that their conversation, his direction, was given to her from within his consciousness. This was no longer a relationship in the ethers. They were talking, planning, loving in every way within this physical dimension now, and they both knew that, when they finally met, there would be no need for words. Their smiles, the knowing that would pass between them, would be that of all that they had experienced. She understood that to reach through the veils of deception was the last part of the journey to bring them finally together within this reality, the reality within which the bliss and perfection of touch, of smell, of taste was to be their blessing.

She stood in the morning sun and looked out across the sea towards Spinalonga Island. He asked her to describe what she saw, and what she saw filled her with a sense of serenity and beauty. For it was as if the ancient knowing of the ocean's depths extended to the surface and appeared in glistening white droplets of wisdoms, of perfection floating above the crest and around this beautiful island that was so sacred, so deeply entrenched within the energy vortex set about it. And as she absorbed the scene ahead, the energies, she understood why she had been destined to complete her book here. The utter perfection of the universal plan never ceased to astonish her. She knew that their coming together would be in perfect timing now, they had discussed it. For the world to truly believe her journey, his journey, they must have irrevocable proof. And the proof lay simply in the fact that, by the time this book was to be read in totality, so much of what she had written about would have come to pass, even that which she had foretold would happen between this moment of now and the end of the year, that which she could not possibly have known, only predicted.

And yet nothing was a prediction, it was her knowing, his knowing, the universe and their soul's direction, and she delighted in the audacious beauty of what lay ahead. She reflected upon how amazing it was to see everybody around her so impassioned, so determined, so utterly knowing of all that was to come to pass. There seemed to be no time now between a thought entering her consciousness and it being manifested instantly into a forward path. Her website was well underway. The solution had been presented with such grace and ease she could hardly believe it. It seemed that everybody she needed was quite literally sent to her instantaneously.

As she spoke to people around her in Crete, they were stunned, inspired and deeply committed to ensuring that the world heard and participated not only in the purchase of her book, but of her vision. She was merely the person to set out the grid of light, to bring these people together to carry out the vision she continually assured everybody around her was the way forward. She was but the conduit, the channel that would draw together the most incredible sense of oneness amongst all those she was to be so privileged to be working with, those she was already so privileged to be working and great friends with now. And she smiled as she thought about *The Secret*, Rhonda Byrnes hugely successful book, film and CD. So often of late, since she first watched that film many weeks ago, she had smiled when she considered that all that had been occurring in her life over this past year had been in precise correlation with that which Rhonda and her team of visionaries, scientists and philosophers had spoken of. In that very moment it occurred to her that they would be delighted to know of yet another case of the living proof of that which they had written about.

* * *

While she was sitting writing on her balcony one morning, Angela texted her from England, saying she felt strongly that Louise should be involved in a worldwide meditation and healing, the Fire the Grid Meditation, that was happening in the next couple of days. She thought that Louise should contact the organiser, Shelley Yates, for she would entirely resonate with what she was doing, as Shelley would with her. They most definitely should be supporting each other's work. Just before Louise had come to Crete, Angela had been drawn to tell her about her overwhelming feeling that she should see Spinalonga Island while she was there, that somehow she and Louise should connect while Louise was at the island. Neither of them knew then what the connection would be, but as she and Angela exchanged texts that morning, a morning when Louise felt so connected to Atlantean energies, to St Germain (the master who was in his lifetimes Francis Bacon, Merlin, Shakespeare, and others) and the knowledge pouring through her consciousness as she wrote so effortlessly to keep up with the flow, she suddenly started to perceive the connection.

For it was that she was being given ancient knowledge once more, utterly filled with the inspiration and expectation that was hers while working in Atlantis.

They had been so expectant, that team of scientists working together, knowing as they worked with the energies that Gaia (the earth's consciousness) worked with them, and supported them. For Gaia graced them with the power of the elements, the vision and understanding of the structure of the universal origins, its sacred geometric structure, its origins beyond the Void, the languages of light from ancient and distant parts, and these scientists, these peoples of Atlantis were utterly at one with all that was. There was no need to further explore travel within their dimension, for all the resources they needed for this were at their disposal. No, they were seeking the means to further the dimensional travel that was already in place. And as the recall began to take hold, Louise felt the overwhelming knowing that had passed between them as they came so close to the answers. Images started to flash through her mind, the source of which she could not determine, but knew to be work left undone.

As she gazed towards Spinalonga Island, she felt the island calling her, the energy calling out to her, seeking her help. There was undoubtedly a connection between this island and Atlantis. For Spinalonga lay in the region between Greece, Egypt, Troy and Libya, all regions which had been claimed by sacred texts as being parts of Atlantis. Louise received another text from Angela, urging Louise to work with her to impart healing upon the island. She was being guided, as were others, to direct Louise to give healing to the island on the day of the 17th July, the day of the Fire the Grid Meditation.

Louise knew that Angela had a deep connection to this island, and somehow her knowing was of a connection with Atlantean times. Once more she pondered the concept that although she was receiving this knowing entirely in this moment of now, in fact, it related to the work she was doing in Atlantis, and that the scientists there would be able to complete the work in Atlantis before the catastrophic fall which had already taken place. For although the fall had taken place, if all occurs in this moment of now then it stands to reason that those from Atlantis who were able to change events, to prevent the corruption which had taken place and restore harmony, could in fact transpose those learnings, finish that work and reinstate Atlantis in its entirety, in the here and now.

Were they to bring forward the teachings of Lemuria as well as Atlantis? The Mayan elder had been so adamant that the Lemurians were the originators of humanity, living in absolute balance and harmony within the universe. The Lemurians were referred to by the Mayans as the Maize People, believed to have inhabited the area now known as Australia. This was the connection, she believed to this island, for she knew some deep and sacred knowledge was stored here. She had felt this last year when the shaft of light had passed through her. She took the children down to the jetty and together they fished in the late afternoon heat. After some time, she stood gazing across directly to the island and an overwhelming urgency came upon her to send healing to this island now.

As she began, the entire island was shrouded in dark and threatening cloud, and St Germain came to her side, reassuring her that now was the perfect moment to begin a series of healings. Instantly the island changed before her eyes. High upon the ridge she saw two distant figures in long white flowing robes that billowed in the wind, and she knew them to be her and Ben. The island beneath their feet began to change colour, first an emerald green, an azure blue sweeping across the plains below, and then the entire vista was awash with silver. Every stone, tree and plain was entirely silver in hue. As she began to draw the healing to a close, St Germain spoke to her. 'Child, there is but another moment of healing to complete.' And so, as she continued, the island lifted into the air within her vision, surrounded in the pitch black of the universal Void, and began to spin around and around, as if held in mid-air by an incredible vortex of energy. As the island spun, a torrent of wind whipped across the sea and around Louise, so strong that she felt herself lift with it. Faster and faster the wind whipped around her, until finally it calmed, and the island was set again into the calm waters. As she opened her eyes she saw the island in all its beauty, completely drenched in sunlight and serenity.

The following day, Louise noticed that several spots had appeared across her torso, together with an incredibly irritating rash. She knew it was somehow connected to the healing she had sent to the island, and resolved to drink plenty of water to flush it through, while asking the universe for help.

The following day was spent with Stefi and the kids at the local beach, taking in the beauty of the sea, basking in the warm Cretan sun, jumping off the jetty into the cool waters and sitting chatting until the sun set magnificently against the backdrop of Spinalonga Island. As they sat chatting, Stefi introduced Louise to Maxim, a charming young Frenchman who was in Plaka on a business studies course. The two of them connected in an instant, much to Stefi's astonished glances, for she had merely said 'Hi,' and exchanged pleasantries in the past. Maxim and Louise knew that this deep connection would draw them together in so many ways through their mutual passion for all that Louise was setting out to achieve. From that moment on, and throughout her stay in Crete, Louise and Stefi found every opportunity when Maxim was not working to be able to talk.

It was while she sat lazily in the sun by the side of a fabulous pool that Louise's next inspiration took form. She wasn't sure if it was the incredible sense of peace she felt as she gazed across the azure waters to the sea and long sandy shores below, or the provocation of her *The Secret* CD she was listening to, or even the result of the download of information she seemed to be receiving at speed from the vortex of energy which rested across her house, but whatever had triggered it, it was most welcome. For she suddenly realised that the principle she was about to apply to her publishing company, that of a founder membership allocation for all who pre-ordered the book within those few weeks, could so readily be transcribed to all aspects of The Ether Group.

 She took out her pen and paper, laughing and trying to keep it dry while being squirted by her boys with their water guns. As she trawled through every aspect of the group being established, the delight which filled her knowing was of the absolute empowerment of inspiration, the empowerment of people's desires to succeed with Ether in establishing all that Ether was to embody; oneness, truth and inspiration, and the desire for the world to be an amazingly inspirational place where everybody's desires became their reality. And as she did so, it seemed that every person was watching her. Her energy radiated now in a way that distracted, mesmerised so many around her. All of her friends out here commented upon it. She knew that these people were seeing Ben's love radiating through her, and even she couldn't help but notice it. Even now she glanced up to see a beautiful young Greek man, whom she had noticed staring at her earlier, utterly beset with a trance-like look upon his face as he watched her intent upon her writing.

 That night, as she excitedly relayed her idea to Stefi, and as her friend relayed how so many upon this island were utterly entranced with Louise's plan, her book, her desire to forge ahead with these changes, they looked up towards the night sky. As Stefi laughed at Louise, bemused as ever with her friend's transformation into scientist, philosopher and poet as she explained evolutionary physics' conceptualisation of cosmic rays, and the current search to determine whether these high-energy cosmic rays could be produced by super-heavy dark matter in the centre of the galaxy, an amazing occurrence began. Fragments of light refracted and then projected up towards the night sky from a distant dip in the valley, leaving a trail of violet hue in their wake. These light shafts then began to dance across the sky, interlocking star structures as they leapt at speed from one star to another. As the light came to rest directly above them, a shaft of light, a shaft of energy, coursed down through Louise, rooting her to the spot where she stood. Some beers later, Louise said goodnight to her friend and lay in bed trying to remember the structures she had seen formed in the sky.

Chapter 23

Angela assured Louise the following morning that she and many others were sending her healing now as they had been directed, knowing that she alone was to stand upon the island of Spinalonga. Angela explained that this morning as she started sending healing, she watched Louise walk out to the island. Archangel Raphael walked with her, holding her and swathing her in a blue light. Little elementals dressed in white surrounded Louise in abundant numbers, swimming to the shores of the island carrying yellow daisies and covering the island in them. She went on to explain that one of her guides, Dorcas, a dolphin from Sirius, emerged from the sea and began downloading codes to Louise, codes that would protect and help her as she sent healing to the island. As she finished explaining this, Louise felt a rush of warm intensity flood her entire being, and a deep sense of being loved.

Early on the morning of the 17th, Louise crept quietly out of the house, leaving the children with Carolyn and her children, who had now arrived for a holiday. She took a speedboat out to the island in order to be there long before any tourists arrived, and as she climbed up the slope of the island, to the place she instinctively knew she needed to reach, an overwhelming feeling filled her senses. At first, she could not place this feeling of the incredible depths of the love of the universe, and yet of disconnection, of separation from a knowing of the deepest truth, to be brought forward to restore oneness. When she reached the top, the warm sea air whipped across the tip of the mound, bringing with it the momentary recall of a time long past, of looking out across the azure seas far below, the wind wildly congruent with the feelings of yearning within her. She looked at the semicircular stone wall set in front of her and knew that she needed to complete it to form a circle of stone.

When she had completed this, she took out the clear quartz crystals she had brought with her, and set three into a pyramid shape in the extremities of the circle, and one in the centre, beneath what was left of an old gnarled tree. She began the healing, St Germain followed by so many masters surrounding her. Ben stood before her and together they understood that it was their combined aura that was to be wrapped around this island. As they did so, a shaft of white light passed through them, down through the centre of the earth. The island became white and silver in hue and an amethyst dome was constructed over them both, so as to shield and protect them it seemed. St Germain then began to speak to them both, and as he did so, it was as if the grief of separation of all the ages was spent high upon that mound, the grief of all humanity coursing through them both as they wrapped their auras entirely around the island, around each other. And they wept as

St Germain spoke to them gently. 'You are but one with the universe, the beginning and the end, the sacred love of you two is the essence of universal truth, of the one, and of that which all of humanity has in its abundant birthright to experience.' And in that moment as they wept they understood this to be so, that their love was of the one, the love of all time. And as Louise spoke of the love that passed between them being so deeply entrenched within the pages of her book, so much of the story that she wrote, Jesus spoke to them both. 'Of course your book is a love story. Do you not see that you are the love of the beginning, the representation of all that was Adam and Eve in conception, of the polarity law of god, and that the world must see this as its key to abundance? The world must experience this through you two and understand that it is their absolute right to experience the love of this kind, divine love.'

As she quietly climbed back down the hillside and made her way towards the jetty at the water's edge, Louise was intent only upon reaching the calm of the sea. There were no words to express the feelings coursing through her being. She sat on the water's edge and threw a shard of crystal into the water, a shard that had come away from one of the crystals she had planted upon the mound. As she did so, a deep connection with the ocean, with the universe, tore at her heart. She called Angela, her words barely audible through her tears. And her friend, moved beyond expression, relayed all that she had experienced through her simultaneous healing. So much had she seen that she promised to write it for Louise, who could not absorb it all at this time. One thing stood out above all, and that was the incredible love that Angela had experienced which had passed between Louise and Ben. His love for her was beyond anything Angela had previously witnessed, and as she explained all that He had asked her to convey to Louise, about a connection that she must explore to a well with running water, a heaviness weighed upon her heart. It was when she finally spoke of seeing him sitting behind a desk in Australia, a deep pain piercing his heart, that Louise began to weep, for she too felt that pain.

She slowly walked back around the island to the jetty where Angelos was waiting in the speedboat to take her home. Back on dry land, she drove slowly back towards the house. As she neared it, she stopped beside a nearby olive grove and took out her 'phone. She had an incredible knowing that she needed to call Him. She would have questioned the motive, the sense, the reasoning at any other time, but now she did not. Somewhere deep within her consciousness her soul was crying out to her, and she dialled his number, knowing that she had intended to wait for Him to call her when He was ready, when He was surrounded by the news of her, her book and her publishing company.

It was the pain she felt deep within, the knowing of His pain that lead her to calmly and quietly leave a message for Him. The message simply told Him that He would soon hear of her book and of all that she would be doing now. She told Him of her publishing company, of its intended international basis, the head office to be based in Sydney, and that from the outset, this was what she had intended to speak to Him about. She quietly hung up, telling Him only to call when He was ready. She knew that He would not call yet; she had no expectations, rather a knowing that the timing was not now. It was only that, somehow, she felt He needed to hear these words, to understand that she was forging ahead with all that was the path to bring them together.

The next two days saw her trying to quell the incredibly tumultuous sway of feelings that had utterly overcome her conscious state. After collapsing into her bed one night, nursing an extremely rare headache, St Germain asked her to write, and so, as ever, she wrote as she was directed:

The Magic of the Cosmos

As stars o'erhead fall through the skies
Deception pulls a varied smile.
For those upon the planet's earth
Do wholly know this tale is worth

A knowing head, conception's truth.
For cosmic rays are element's truth,
They bring the knowing of those who tread
The highest mentioned light and thread.

The matter of the darkness know
Is all we think, we care to show,

To truly uncover all that lies
Beneath the stars, amongst the skies.

How may consciousness take hold
Of notions thread, reality unfold?
As through the veils of time and life
We close our eyes. Behold this knife,

This knife which cuts all vision through
Is like the light I hold to you,
The beacon of the path to truth.
Restore once more your only youth.

For evolution is the name
Of Gaia's crazy, heavenly game.
It's no use here once truth we feel,
For understand now what is real.

I am the master bright and true,
The very one beheld in you,
Who motions to the highest thread,
Pulls you gently from your bed,

Then catapults the notion through
As if propulsion is but hue.
For I smile now as knowing spreads
And stars become your guiding thread,

Those cosmic rays which burn so bright.
For under skies which dark, they might

Bring thoughts of nearing earth's full end.
But circles, cycles never end.

We are but one, oh child of law,
For never is the open door
A moment of the vision's end,
For life is utter beauty, friend.

Once you know the secret here,
Feel solution, watch it near,
It fills you ever with the bliss
Of all that falls upon a kiss.

For stars they kiss the cosmic fall,
The energy for which they stall,
The ever growing fall or thread
Of heavens feel, dimensions head.

Magic is but love and light
The eyes they open, bring the sight.
Those notions which appear just once
Are dimensions' gift, the gift of trust.

Ech bin meneth im bith mere
Hush pin ente um bener
Ich men him honar um banar
Ente ente him hintar.

As soon as she put the pen down and finished writing, Louise fell instantly into a deep and heavy slumber.

The next morning the tumultuous feelings had not yet abated. She began to question everything, until finally, after yet another long telephone conversation with Julie about all the things they were organising for the book and the website, an understanding so overwhelming began to dawn upon her, upon them both. For it was, they both realised, that whenever Louise had these periods, something quite profound always became apparent to her. And the dawning of this light was to utterly change her path forward. In this moment she understood that, far from her having believed all this time that she was seeking her twin soul, that she had co-created this path with the universe to bring them together, she finally understood that in fact, it had been Him that had sought *her* out.

When she considered every step she had ever taken, it had been utterly based upon trust, trust of her soul's instruction, trust in the beauty of the path that had quite literally unfolded before her. She had been responding to the universal signs, not dictating them. Had He not told her so many times that it was He, not she, who called her to Him when she first encountered the Ben in town and started upon the path of recollection? Had He not dictated the most staggering and eloquent poetry to her in declaration of His love for her across time? Was it not He who pleaded with her not to walk away from Him and their union back in January? Was it not the case that the universe had given her this incredible book to write, the message to deliver, leaving her in a state of wonder and blessing that she was to be within the centre of this story as it unfolded about her? Was it not the universe that had left her signs along the way to determine that this man was her path ahead: the article and picture in the London Book Fair magazine, the evidence set out at Les Labadous, the way that everything was falling into place with such grace and ease in the establishment of the publishing company and the media group as the first parts of Ether?

She had, inadvertently, declared but one thing to the universe. To walk her path in grace, ease and in utter completion, asking only for the abundant love of her twin soul, the highest level of love, in return. The universe had steered her along a path that was entirely focussed upon a certain end, an end that brought her to Him. For as surely as she sat beneath the shade of an olive tree, which cast its shadow across her incredulous expression, the understanding was dawning upon her now. She had been so sure that, once they met, He would have the other half of this incredible story to tell, that which had unfolded before Him. She was now beginning to understand what that truly meant. For was she not about to deliver to Him not only one of the most widely read and distributed books in history, but also the publishing company He had undoubtedly intended to establish and run, this publishing company of hers which, together with the rest of the Ether Media Group, would revolutionise publishing in its current state? As this knowledge and understanding sank in, Louise realised that no longer was she on a trail of searching, but she was quite literally being brought to her path. The universe was bringing to her in utter perfection all that she had chosen, all that He had chosen in the perfection of the laws of attraction so beautifully presented within *The Secret* book.

And then the torrent of universal messages began once more. Late that evening she took the children out on a speedboat trip. Intending for Angelos to take them, when they arrived he presented his brother, Georgos, who would take them while he continued with windsurfing instruction. Louise had never met Georgos, and as they sped across the sea, the boys shrieking with delight as the boat tossed about upon the surf, they began to talk. From the moment they began she understood this to be no coincidental meeting. Georgos was fascinated with her story, as was she with his.

He had quite determinedly changed the path his life was taking after just a short while ago fixing his intention upon the path he was now following. Having completed his studies in shipping at university in England, it was only now that he had focused upon using what he had learnt there to determine a path as an officer of a shipping company. He had recently purchased, after a chance meeting, a company that would transform seawater into pure water in order to supplement the water already aboard his ships. They talked at length about intention creating reality, and both smiled and laughed when he declared that, having just returned from Alaska and here for only a couple of weeks, his next ship, one he had just purchased, was called *The Quest*. Louise promised to come back over the next couple of days so that he could take them on a trip out beyond the coastline to a place of beauty, in the sea beneath some ancient rocks where they could snorkel, dive, where the waters so clear and deep bore witness to many amazing fish and sea creatures.

Two days later she bumped into Georgos on the beach, and he agreed to take her and the children on the boat with him that afternoon. As Louise jumped off the boat beneath the rocks, snorkelled with her friend and the children, basked in the warmth of the sea, she felt the sun strong upon her, infiltrating her senses. They laughed and swam for a few hours, and on their way back to the island, the hot wind whipping about them, their hair blowing wildly, Louise noticed that they were trailed by a stunning rainbow which glowed upon the sea's crest and up into the azure sky above.

But the next evening she lay in bed, utterly bereft of joy, feeling as if the depths of separation were upon her. Why was she questioning like this? Ben was with her continually, the universe was sending her constant signs, the book, marketing and website were progressing with grace and ease, and all around her were excitedly chatting and anticipating the huge success ahead. Stefi had managed to line up a whole team overnight to run Ether's first retreat centre in Crete, and Louise had already asked the universe that, if it be in the highest good, they may have the retreat on or near to the island of Spinalonga, in honour of its beauty, grace, deep energetic connection to Atlantis, and the energetic vortex around it, which provided the perfect base for communion with oneself, the

perfect base for a retreat. Much was happening back in
England to facilitate the path ahead. Louise knew that
these dips always preceded deep understanding, and
yet had she not already been given to understand that
her quest was that of a trail, beset by the universe, by her
lover, the path to oneness?

She lay in bed and He spoke to her softly. He asked
her to relay to Him all that was in her consciousness, all
that she had been considering over the last few days.
And as she did so, as clarity fell upon her musings, she
finally understood that here was the understanding
intended for her now. She watched the tears fall across
His face as He, so moved by her recital of her conclu-
sions, her observations, so relieved that finally she
was coming to a point of utter understanding, looked
towards the point of the congruence of their path, of
their coming together now. For it was that this would
only be possible with complete understanding of what
lay ahead. And she, through her tears and her smiles,
spoke of all that lay within her heart.

She spoke of circles and cycles of time, of creation,
of reinventing cycles of life for different plains of existence. She talked of the Atlantean and Lemurian energy
grids and ley lines which lay across Ireland, Australia
and parts of Greece, of the need to reset the balance of
the fabric of the ether over the energy vortexes to allow
the higher vibrations of the dimension of those plains
of existence to take hold here once more, within this
reality. She spoke of how Lemuria and Atlantis represented the beginning of the cycle of life, of humanity

within this plain of existence, and of how this cycle was in existence entirely simultaneously with all beginnings and endings. She spoke of the polarity law of God, and that it represented the beginning and the end of creation's cycles, of completion and of new beginnings being brought to new ends. Every time a cycle completed, she mused, a new beginning raised the vibration of that plane of existence.

She spoke of the Mayans, of the manner in which they lived within cycles of creation, each day in creation carrying a different and unique energy. She spoke of the fact that every time a cycle completes and the vibrations become higher, humanity begins to live in a different plane of existence. She explained that the breath of Gaia was actually about these cycles of life, that once the cycles reached the highest level of vibration within this reality, there would be an outbreath, and the cycle would begin again. These high-energy cosmic rays were in fact reflective of the increasing vibrations that were to enable this cycle to turn, to end. And then, as she forged the link with the quantum field, parallel realities entering into different spheres of vibrational levels, she understood where this was leading. Atlantis was not only the beginning but also the end of this cycle, the beginning and end of every cycle, for it represented all that was the bliss of existence at the highest level, at one with the universe and all that is.

The understanding of the zero-point energy field, the embracing of quantum physics, was a means to increase the vibrational level of this reality within this moment of now, a means to an awareness of realities within cycles of varying vibrational levels. By turning each circle, the bliss of that cycle's earliest days, living in the purest state at one with all that is, we would be able now to experience once more all that is and ever was intended as divinity, as heaven upon earth. In so many records, Atlanteans bred with 'Gods from the skies' to create the highest levels of wisdom. These gods were of course people from the cycles of time, those from different planes of existence taking back the knowledge over-and-over so as to recreate the bliss of all that is, the future and the past replaying in continuous cycles to transpose the ever-increasing levels of understanding and oneness with the universe.

Holistic science was proving this within the Super String Theory. Morphic resonance was entirely representative of the universal mind and various experimental studies substantiated the existence of morphic resonance, a kind of holographic memory. Now she truly understood that, of course, the devastating fall of Atlantis could be avoided for, within this cycle, it was not just the beginning but the end and the end could encapsulate the entire journey of all of the cycles, to ensure that the work being carried out was indeed harmoniously aligned with the universe, with the divinity of oneness. In that moment Louise understood that her lover had come back to her so many times, across so many cycles of creation, and was reaching out to her once more to guide her, to lead her and bring her to a point of clarity, of understanding so that she could indeed do the same for Him. For their journey now was deeply embedded in the knowledge they had pursued, had sought across creation, of the ancient teachings and beyond these cycles of creation, those from which originated the languages of light.

Days later, as the universe began to bring inspiration upon inspiration to direct her path for marketing the book, the synergies continued to fall gracefully into place. Full-page advertisements in *The Sunday Times* needed a serious abundance to run but, 'Hey', she thought, 'it's the universe's job to deliver the abundance'. She was being asked daily now to join Internet-based groups which would give her book huge coverage: social networking sites for scientific groups, book societies and groups all around the globe who resonated entirely with all she was setting out to achieve.

It was as she mulled over this, together with the US-based marketing she had instigated with Pavel, that Ben spoke of what He intended to do to raise the profile of this book. As He explained to her, she could hardly believe what she was hearing. Over and over she asked Him to repeat what He had said, utterly incredulous that He would do such a thing. For the very thing He intended was not only to offer absolute proof to the world that she was utterly authentic in all that she had written about their union, but also the most honouring and beautiful declaration to her of His intent.

* * *

The last four days of her holiday were spent in a beautiful little bohemian house on the beach, looking straight across the sea towards Spinalonga Island. These days were blissful, writing to the sound of the waves lapping beneath her bedroom window, the bougainvillea and oleander in the garden below, framing the view of Spinalonga in the background as she looked across the sea, drinking and laughing with friends through the early hours of the morning, and being utterly at one with her lover in the most romantic setting she could have anticipated.

One morning, as she headed off to an Internet café to look at the web, book and promotional designs, she suddenly had the urge to research a little more about her ring. She was astounded at what she found. Serious research had been completed by a Harvard student called Katherine Forsyth, by various scholars researching early and ancient Celtic script and by the designer of her ring, Sheilagh Fleet. She had known of the ring's unique design and rarity when she had first tried to repurchase it. Why had she not looked at this before? And yet as the knowing panned out before her she understood why, for she realised that the significance of what she was reading could not have been fully appreciated until this moment of now. And as Louise considered that she had two rings, one for her and one for Ben, the significance of the research she was reviewing rocked her to the core.

The inscriptions upon her ring were ancient ogham script, which was believed to be one of the first Celtic scripts, predating the Viking period, in approximately 500 AD, and was referred to as The Celtic Tree Alphabet. This script contained twenty letters in the alphabet, all very distinctive in their etchings. The script was very informal, with sketch-like incisions scratched into the surface of items. The alphabet began with Louise and Ben's initials, and the ogham writings were always written in a circular manner, clockwise in direction (highly congruent with the circles or cycles of creation). The inscription upon her ring was a direct copy of the inscription upon the whorl stone, which was a circular stone made from fine-grained, cream coloured limestone with a quartz grain, and literally translated into 'Blessing on the Soul'. The letters at the beginning and the end of the translation, sitting next to each other upon the whorl stone, so tightly knitted as almost to be mistaken as one letter instead of two, were her and Ben's initials. The first three letters of the translation, 'Ben', spelt his name in full.

Ogham script had been used for divination. In *Tochmarc Étaíne*, a tale in the Mythological Cycle in Irish literature, she read that the druid Dalan took four wands of yew and wrote ogham letters upon them. He then used them as tools for divination in much the same manner as neo-pagans and modern druids use them today. A series of sticks were created, one for each letter, and used within the divination process. Each letter had a meaning associated with a tree, a plant and with a Latin origin. She went on to read that in past times, ogham letters were thought to bestow a magical, talismanic energy when incised onto personal belongings.

Louise sat back as the full implications of the understanding in front of her coursed through her senses. She had been drawn to that ring so long ago; her soul had quite literally taken her to it. She remembered the trance-like state in which she had been driven to purchase it, intent upon not leaving that castle shop until the assistant had searched everywhere to try and find a second ring that may fit her. She had been wearing upon her being from that moment on, as she had never since removed this ring, the blessing of her return to sacred union, in every way bestowed upon her with the guidance and support of the ancient Celts. For she and Ben were joined upon this ring, at the very beginning and end of the inscription, in much the same way that they represented the very beginning of creation's cycle within the Mayan teachings, He being born under Imox, the carrier of time which represented the beginning of the cycle of creation of the cosmos, and she under B'atz, the beginning of the cycle of creation of humanity.

So much more cyclical evidence was relevant to them within the Mayan teachings, teachings that were not yet to be in the public domain. In addition, she read on, the jewellery design Skyran actually meant 'to shine, to glitter brightly'. She considered how deep an affiliation she had always felt with the druids, and so many ancient Celtic practices and, once more, felt the links to Ireland which had so deeply rooted her consciousness to that land for so long now. She knew beyond doubt, and delighted in the knowing that this other ring was to be bestowed upon Ben, along with its intent and grace, so soon now.

* * *

That evening, after a day of writing, Louise wandered around the little house, admiring the images, photographs and paintings upon its walls. This house had, since the moment she had stepped foot across the boundary, felt like home to her, so resonant were the energies with her. As she smiled affectionately at a photograph of an elderly Australian gentleman on the wall, the now-deceased previous owner of the house, she felt a huge affinity with his quite evident love of life. She thanked him for allowing her to stay in his beautiful house, and as she felt this connection grow, he began to talk to her. He spoke to her in such a manner which made her truly laugh, filling her with a sense of a man utterly in control, paternal and yet driven to experience life to the full, pragmatic and yet altogether wise.

After explaining to her a little of men's logic, of its difference to women's, of the need to accept that a man will choose to do what is necessary to do as and when it is necessary and not inform you prior to the event that he will be taking such action, he asked her to apply this to her situation with her 'young Australian man' as he put it.

'Know that if he tells you now, which he has, that he
will be meeting you so soon now, in the manner in
which he has suggested, then, my dear, he will do just
that. You need no phone calls to tell you that now is
not the time for contact. Know that he will call you
precisely when the time is right.'

She laughed as she was being berated momentarily for any lapse in her belief in all that was happening
now. He then asked her to pick up a pen and paper and
to write exactly what it was that he was about to tell
her. And she wrote:

The cosmos is a collection of obscure and yet obvious codes and derivations of the universe's intent to
utterly confuse, and yet clarify the extreme element of
each reality. Each dimension has its own unique iden-
tifying cosmos, set of modular symbols and perpen-
dicular constructs, that is to say that the constructs,
compiled, of course, of energy, are utterly bizarre and
yet linear, and therefore ordered in their structure. The
linear structure, when examined under a microscope,
would prove to be fractal. That is because all elements
of the cosmos at any point in a given creation and cycle
are fractal.

Evolutionary science must start to focus upon the cosmic intent rather than the cosmic content. That is to
say that the intention of the cosmic rays, the intent
upon which they are focussed, is highly and completely
reflective of the intent upon which they were born.

We are talking of course about dark matter. Quantum physics should be working in the area of understanding the fractal element of parallel dimensions, and not focussed upon this dimension. Cosmic rays are born upon the intent created outside of this cosmos. Understand this and you've cracked the basis for dimensional travel. Breakthrough Propulsion Physics – you've written about this, you know why it is out of kilter right now. In terms of the study, scientists do not yet fully understand the quantum field, the zero-point energy field. To understand this they must do as I've said and study the fractal element of dimensions outside of this cosmos.

He went on to explain many things, which he asked her to commit to her *Book of Knowledge*. These explanations should be shared with Ben to whom, he said, they would not be new. They were not, right now, to be in the public domain. He went on to say that he would be with her now, as a guide, and much more would be discussed in the days and months to follow. He was insistent upon the fact that he would choose her to make this home her home, and laughed as he said 'You will be back here soon my dear, with your Australian man.' They made a pact. He would help her ensure that her book was sold to so many millions of people over these next months, and she would, with part of the abundance, purchase his home and keep it entirely in the manner in which she found it now, to preserve its beauty and radiant energy.

That evening, under the full moon, she and Stefi sat and conspired for many hours. At some time in the late hours, Louise took a clear quartz crystal that she had brought with her from Les Labadous and, tracing a line from a disused well next to the house, walked to the seashore and cast the crystal into the waters. The well, she determined, may have been that which Angela had seen during the healings upon Spinalonga and, knowing that the well had some significance upon that which was to come to pass now, she understood that the ritual under the full moon was appropriate. As she looked upon the metal structure above the well, an arch, either side of which were set seven thistles and below them a pair of angel wings, the connection to Les Labadous was all too apparent.

Her final night in Plaka was spent with her friends, Stefi and Karen, talking under the stars. When Karen left and Maxim came to join them, they began to discuss how much he missed his girlfriend. And so it was that Louise began to explain to them the incredible union she shared with Ben, of their ability to be one, of how that could be the same for Maxim and his girlfriend, and of its relevance to the relationship experienced between Mary Magdalene and Jesus, and of all those who practised the Sex Magic of Isis, that which was so beautifully and eloquently transcribed in Tom Kenyon and Judy Sion's *The Magdalene Manuscript*. Stefi and Maxim resolved to order *The Magdalene Manuscript* immediately in order to understand how they too could achieve this incredible union, so as to be together and at one with their partners at all times.

Louise walked home, utterly held and loved by her sacred partner, into the dimly lit house and threw open the window of her bedroom to the night sky and the sea ahead. As she gazed upwards, once again considering the astonishing and honouring manner in which Ben had told her He was about to come together with her now, a shooting star quite suddenly appeared through the night sky, darting in and out of this reality for just a few seconds as it streaked across the sky.

Chapter 24

Finishing her book was an interesting process for Louise, for it felt, at this point, that all that she believed would come to pass was that which graced the pages she was writing. And yet, she considered, had the universe not brought all to her in a manner in which it had foretold? Christian had called to tell her that the building work had started on the house, and so, by the time she arrived home, all was well underway. Not bad, she thought, for someone who has only been in her house for four weeks. The universe was clearly intent upon settling her home in preparation for all that was to come. And there, within the pages of the *New Scientist*, which she had sat down to read, was an article that made her laugh so, for here were scientists speculating about the very aspects that she had been writing about, dimensional travel. An article devoted to the neutrinos that were poised to unlock the door to the 'Theory of Everything' made her smile. As she read, it was as if St Germain was smiling with her. As a knowing passed between them she read on:

> When Heinrich Päs checked his mail on 11 April this year, he was in for a surprise. Just months earlier, he had suggested that neutrinos (subatomic

particles) might have the ability to travel through time. Now he was getting a deluge of mail from fellow physicists pointing out the spooky similarity between his predictions and some experimental results published earlier that day. The experiment called Miniboone was being run by a team of nearly 80 physicists at the Fermi National Accelerator Laboratory at Illinois and the results presented a puzzle. They simply didn't match what everyone thought they knew about neutrinos, and in a quest for an explanation physicists were resorting to a variety of exotic ideas, time travel among them. But what really got physicists excited was the possibility that the findings could reveal a gap in the standard model of particle physics and point the way to a 'theory of everything' that unites Einstein's general theory of relativity and quantum theory.

The article went on to suggest the possible existence of a fourth neutrino. Päs studied neutrinos from the perspective of string theory, and his deduction was that these fourth neutrinos (sterile neutrinos) took short cuts through one of the normally invisible higher dimensions that string theory provides for, and so appear to travel through time. An experiment called Nova was now being established, which would take two to three years to complete, and would fire a beam of neutrinos to determine their behaviour and whether or not they changed, therefore determining whether they travel through time and dimensions. She considered the cosmic intent and particle physics' place in determining intent outside of the cosmos, that is intent being created from dark matter beyond the universe. Of course, she knew that dark matter was intent, was the very consciousness coming into form as the form was creating the consciousness itself. Morphic resonance was entirely representative of the universal mind. It represented all that was the patterning which overlays the quantum chaotic field to bring similarity of form into being. It was interesting that right now the field phenomenon was being used to prove teleconnetic abilities, telepathy and multiple dimensions. She considered the information she had been given for her Book of Knowledge, and the terminology now being presented by science as neutrinos being keys to unlock the secrets of the universe and she smiled.

Two days later, Angela called Louise, astonished at the manner in which she had been resting in her garden, basking in the rays of the English summer sun, when she had quite suddenly received a message from Ben to be passed on to Louise. This message, He had explained, concerned a matter of urgency, and was a puzzle that was to unlock the manner in which a final barrier, a veil of deception, was to be removed so as to bring them together. As she read the message, she was utterly at a loss. That night as she found herself despairing for her lack of understanding, she began to truly question all that was happening to her. It was only the following morning, once a calm had descended upon her, that she reread the message and began to piece together the puzzle. The message read:

> *I am a flying vortex. I long to fly to you. The sound of love is all around, but for me it is not enough. To reach the soul that is also me is a task almost too much to bear. Help me, my beloved, my dearheart, to see what lies beyond. Don't you see the land is far, far away that I may not see? Make the land a veil away and bring your heart to me. The sound of love is a frequency, love to my musical ear. Go softly my love, for the sound must match – the cosmos – our love refined. Do not take away this need I have for a love that soars above; you are our creation, within your soul is the answer, my love.*

> *There is a stone of beautiful magic within your energy – create the magic of a bygone time and let the universe alight within the colour, the sound that has no equal for it is the sound of creation. I return, my love to a place of being, awaiting that sound of love.*

She suddenly realised that the stone of magic within her energy that he spoke of, was of course the incised whorl stone, the copy of which she wore on her finger (in fact twice as she was now wearing both rings within her energy). As she searched once more through the information supplied in the Harvard research on the ogham script, she read a fact, which astonishingly, she had missed before. The translation actually read 'a blessing on the soul of L'. In that moment she understood that Ben had incised that message himself. It was their pledge across time and space to one another, their troth before the universe. This whorl stone had been excavated and discovered in the same year that He had been born and she read that whorl stones had been incised with a message by a man for his sweetheart. The clues within his message about the cosmos were, she believed, that the exact replica of this ogham inscription could be seen as a star system of another dimension. This was a portal, and the sound frequency he had asked her to determine was, in fact, the frequency of that other dimension.

As she discussed this with both Christian and Angela, much fell into place, and they determined to help Louise find the answer. Christian had already been given a sound frequency as he had received her original message while sounding within a group, using the golden mean, the sound and structure of creation's point, and had worked with that original sound. She knew that they were traversing realities, cycles of creation, to bring together knowledge. They were piecing together the puzzle of the knowledge that would bring creation's beginning to completion, to bring harmony to the cycles of creation, to prevent the initial and disastrous fall of Atlantis.

And so it was that the path to establishing her book and the Ether Foundation was catapulted forward. Time, she continually repeated to all around her, was an illusion. However it seemed that the universe really had determined to ensure all happened in this moment of now. Within just a few weeks her website was established as was the book design, the most incredible set of marketing campaigns were set in place, and the firm foundation of the Ether Publishing company and Ether Music productions was laid out. The momentum behind the book was so huge she could almost be forgiven for pinching herself. She knew, and always had known, that the intention was for this book to be in the public domain now, and that she need only follow her soul's instruction, her intuition, as the universe co-created all of the amazing synergies unfolding to ensure that her book was indeed widely available in the public domain. And yet she still marvelled at how, when given over entirely to the universe to construct, the momentum and the path fell so easily into place.

She also recognised that the universe's timing was always perfection and that the way in which the results were delivered could only result in the miracles the universe intended when handed over entirely without expectation. The entire Ether Media Group was taking shape so quickly. Life became a whirlwind. And yet it was during that time that Louise had to come to terms with the parting from a friend who had been so dear to her. As the reasons for their parting had become so evident, she further understood that on occasion, the hardest path to pursue was the one pursued in love and truth. And as for she and Ben, the world was at once both shocked and astonished at the manner in which they finally came together.

Chapter 25

As Louise stood, waiting for her cue to step out onto the stage at Wembley, her thoughts began to drift back over these past years, those which had led her to this moment of now. How was it possible that the bliss of all that she had beheld, the path that she and Ben had trodden in unison since their first meeting, together with all those who had come together to create the foundation, could have created so magnificently change beyond all vision, within such a short space of time. And yet, she smiled knowingly, acknowledging that which she so readily repeated to so many, that time is merely an illusion and all is created in its magnificence from this moment of now. She had been told by so many that she must be prepared for the years to follow, for all that was to come to pass, and they had, of course, been so right.

The Sacred Quest had proven extraordinarily successful, sought after by so many of the world's publishers, becoming one of the most widely read books in the world, second only to the book released by Ben so soon afterwards. His book exquisitely detailed His own path, the synchronicities and astonishing universal direction that had been laid out before Him, his understanding and experience of their coming together, their union, and all that was their combined path ahead. The world had so readily sought this chapter, so eloquently and articulately delivered with the passion and authenticity of someone who had quite evidently transcribed his experiences as He was living them, especially after the extraordinary way in which He had declared his love for her, had wed her in sacred union.

Louise smiled as she relived the first moment they touched, the moment in which He declared to her, and to the world, all that was His abiding love for her. As she had waited for Ben at the arrivals lounge, their souls utterly entranced by the knowing of their coming together, He had asked strangers to bestow white flowers upon her at the very moment when he asked her to marry Him. Then, at Chalice Wells, they had wed in sacred union by the well, the very same well where she had been told by Jesus that he would preside over their union, the Vesica Piscis, the very depiction of all that was their abiding love, the universal love, by their side.

Ether Publishing had gone on to become the first truly international, non-discriminatory publisher, the people's publisher. The head office had, as Louise had foreseen, been established in a stunning office overlooking the waters of Sydney Harbour and the Sydney Opera House, where she knew Ben to have been standing only moments ago. From the moment it was established, it seemed that every author, hugely successful as well as those who were as-yet unknown, discovered their passion for the entitlement of the people to have their right to live their inspiration. Ether became the publisher of choice for all, providing the ability for all to publish through many different media. People were enthralled at the opportunity to purchase books set to music, music of such a kind that had not been heard within the public domain to that point. This music reached so many individuals who, otherwise, would not have picked up a book to read, or even considered listening to an audio book.

The fact that Ether Music, driven by Matt, produced these soundtracks as audio and soundtracks alone, set in multiple media, meant that the message reached the world in all formats. For it was of course that, with the intent that music being the language of feeling would bring about an understanding of the entire book's message even without the necessity to hear or understand the words of the story, that the entire population did indeed receive the messages. And this music brought back the true essence (much of which was being brought back from Atlantean understanding) of all that had ever been intended. It changed the face of the music experience. People were finally able to understand the true essence of feeling, as opposed to merely hearing. Matt had, himself, become one of the most successful musicians in the world, as readily predicted, changing the face of music entirely.

The Ether Charitable trust ensured that through narrative and music conferencing, all areas of the globe were reached. Ether Productions had got off the ground so quickly, initially producing the various series they had planned, all of which had been commissioned by

TV stations including Ether TV. The company then went on to produce an inspirational news channel, which truly changed the face of news presentation. Yes, they had received fierce opposition in some areas to the messages they were portraying through this channel. They were in many cases, entirely contradicting those representations that were broadcast by the mainstream news channels. Louise had been intent upon this from the outset, so intent upon children and adults having the right to understand the beauty that was evident in every situation, the balance, and the right to recreate their reality through their own thoughts, that she positively welcomed the fierce reaction. For it was that the population at large spoke for itself. Their news channel had become the most widely watched, so much so that there had been continual demands to expand the material being filmed, and to involve the population at large in providing material as witnesses to the amazing and inspirational acts being carried out the world over.

The films produced, the first of which had been *The Sacred Quest*, which had scooped many awards, had enabled many people to realise their dreams of seeing their vision become a film. As with Ether Publishing, all the bureaucracy that was in place within an industry intent upon prevention rather than creation of the right to expression, had been swept aside. Authors did not sign over rights to the Ether Group for the production of films, music or any other activity relating to the original script or book. They rather offered the group first refusal on an equitable basis, where Ether would be obliged to provide a competitive bid for the individual's consideration. This equality, balance and freedom of the individual's expression, ensured that this group truly did become the people's first choice, and had enforced a huge shift within the existing industries.

So many incredible people had stepped forward to become involved in the Ether Group – so passionate it seemed was the call from within for so many individuals, already driving change in certain areas, to consolidate and work amongst visionaries, those quite clearly co-creating with the universal source – that Ether continued to attract the most amazing visionaries. And the group was widespread in its achievements.

Within mere months the Ether Retreats Group had been established, the first retreat being established in Crete, on a plot of land overlooking Spinalonga Island. Many around the world came forward to join the Ether Retreat Group, bringing with them their own retreats, situated in the most incredible locations, those entirely conducive to discovering the very essence of oneself, the journey to within and to reconnection with all that was the universal truth, reconnection to the universe itself. The Ether Cafés, cool and funky, ethnic, and serving organic and ethically sourced products, were truly successful now. These offered a new way of being, of music, food, drink, and new technological entertainments, all encompassed within a complete alternative to existing bars or cafés. These cafés were integral to many of Ether's retreats, healing centres and shops, and became the basis of food supply within the new schooling and wellness centres. The healing centres had been established in their multitude, once again being joined by so many who, already practising and understanding some of these universal practices being embraced and brought to the fore through the Ether Group, had determined to be part of it.

Wellness centres to replace medical centres had been revolutionary in their approach, and, while initially attracting scepticism through mainstream media's messages, had been readily embraced by so much of the population around the world, that the move towards these as centres of choice was rapid. It seemed that the impassioned doctors and doctrines of mainstream medicine were in fact entirely in agreement with the ethos being set by the reality of people creating their health through their intention, understanding all too well that medicine was about removing disease. Science, philosophy, medicine, spirituality and universal energetic understanding were merging their abilities to address and recreate balance in all things.

No longer was there the fear associated with entering a hospital and all that might come to pass upon the pursuit of a course of medical action, for hospitals were no more. They had been replaced by harmonised centres, where patients were to be brought to a sense of oneness, of balance through so many practices, many of which totally eradicated the need for mainstream medicine of any kind. The pioneering surgery that was introduced was exactly that, carried out only when absolutely necessary, and operated entirely in harmony with all other practices. So many pioneers of medical science had been berated for their desire to bring the creation of life via genetic science. The world had finally moved on to an understanding that in reality, the physical form was merely a fraction of the energetic make up of an individual, of a soul, and that if a soul chose to inhabit a life form of any kind, it was that soul's choice, entirely resonant with the path it chose. Humanity could create a form, but not a life. And thus it had been that so many pioneers, within many areas of medicine, had so readily become involved with the Ether Group, its charitable trust funding ever-increasing ways of drawing together new forms of healing with the science of energetic oneness. The Atlantean healing practices had been brought back in their entirety.

Conference centres were abundant around the globe now. After the initial reaction to *The Sacred Quest*, to the premise of universal truth and oneness transcending all organised religion, many had determined to become part of a growing desire to understand and live their life in absolute pursuit of bliss. Understanding, finally, that the only universal law was love, gave the release so many had required, desired, the license to live their life in the way it had always been intended. When Louise considered the people who had stepped forward to pioneer these conference centres with the Ether Group, to bring to the group the amazing work they had been carrying out for some time now, she felt a deep sense of pathos. Some of them she had been deeply moved by when she had met them. One man, a true visionary, had infused her heart, as he spoke in his dulcet tones, with a sense of the knowing of all that had befallen her, of her path as she walked hand in hand with the universe. It was with great joy, she reflected, that he had asked to work with their team to take these conference centres and their teachings out to areas of the globe devoid of any such teachings right now, truly bringing together an understanding of science and spirituality, of the oneness of the universe, of all creation's cycles, of dimensional realities and the understanding through science of all that is the universe.

As people began to understand sound and structure as the elements of energy, so they began to bring together a knowing of the harmonious balance of the land, the people and all of creation's cycles being at one. Using the pioneering technology developed within their technology group, these conference centres had ensured that all people had access to the knowledge imparted through scientists and spiritual teachers alike. These were centres where evolutionary science had a platform from which to become utterly and irrevocably entwined with the growing understanding of the nature of the soul, of the energy of oneness. As such, the rapid moves towards a level of existence where all people were finally able to use all of their telekinetic abilities, was fast approaching, for science was now utterly committed to bringing about such change, such remembrance.

Louise delighted at being so heavily involved with the scientific centres the group had established. Through the work they had been carrying out, they were so close now to achieving that which she had been told would come about, dimensional travel. So much of the basis of this had stemmed from the extraordinary universal information she and some others had been given and were continuing to receive, which she had diligently kept within her *Book of Knowledge*, and which was now being used in conjunction with evolutionary science. Her guides had become abundant and their knowledge extraordinary. Finally, science and spirituality had utterly converged, with those who had pioneered such changes driving evolutionary science forward. No longer were studies separated, and ancient teachings of civilisations such as the Maya, were integral to the understanding of the basic principles of science.

These centres were positioned in vortexes around the globe, those where the fabric of the ether had been gently teased apart before. Cosmology, quantum studies, particle physics, astrophysics and philosophy were explored in unison with astral weather, Sacred Geometry and other Atlantean sciences, including the use of crystals and quasi-crystals. As in the Atlantean practices, those working within these scientific centres were to bring together years of extremely demanding study with meditation, in order to harmonise intellect and intuition. All of the scientists now underwent study to expand their awareness and improve their psychic abilities. They were taught to trust their intuition as well as the laws of science. This had produced remarkable and universally harmonious steps forward in so many

areas – energy, travel, healing, communications, technology, agriculture and so on.

An Ether Academy had been established, bringing
to the fore a completely new and revolutionary type of
schooling which had been readily embraced across the
globe. Some had chosen to absorb part of the teachings
within their own schooling systems. Many new schools
had been established to wholly embrace the entire way
of being. Not only was the curriculum radically different
from traditional schooling, the structure and manner of
teaching was also changed to accommodate the ability
to work and learn driven by one's inspiration. Ancient
practices were reinstated which utterly absorbed and
captivated the students. Quasi-crystals were used in
the classroom to record data, and students were taught
to work with these crystals, learning to understand and
control the power of the self, of thought. Competition
was eradicated and replaced with a desire to extend
one's very essence, to bring forth the deepest desires
to achieve one's individual greatness, to explore the
wonder of now. Meditative practices and the essential nature of being still, of creating from the moment,
underpinned the entire ethos. Children were no longer
labelled as troublesome, as having ADHD and other
such disorders, but rather recognised and brought to
an awareness of their sense being within this reality.
They were brought to an understanding and celebrated
for their amazing gifts for others now to understand,
at a time when others had begun to understand that all
realities were merging into one.

With tears in her eyes, Louise began to consider the many thousands of lives that had been so radically changed around the globe through the production centres Ether had established, in unison with others already established. These centres had taken children from the streets, clothed, housed, fed and trained them with skills. They had brought the Ether Academy to these areas, providing schooling of a revolutionary nature to all they could accommodate. This had increased dramatically over just a short space of time, as so many investors and people had come forward to support this area of the group. Children had been taken from areas where they had been beaten or used for sport by local constabularies, and were instead brought back to a sense of their being, of their greatness and of their abundant right to the grace and bliss of life. Through the power of creative thought they had become able to redesign their own lives.

The extensive number of Ether Shops around the globe served two purposes. One was to bring organically produced and ethically sourced, energetically harmonised products to the people, to aid with a complete way of living at one with the universe. The second was to provide an outlet for those products produced within the Ether Group, by the production centres, publishing and music groups, in order to reinvest the profits within the charitable trust and therefore reinvent the cycle and perpetuate the growth and work carried out by the trust. It was incredible, she thought, how the world-at-large, so inspired by the notion that they owned a part of this group, continually increased the funding to this charitable trust. Even large corporations and local governments were now diverting profits from taxation into this charitable trust, pledging time and other facilities to help orchestrate many of the activities being undertaken. It seemed that the world was coming to understand that the inspiration resulting from being a part of one, was so much greater than that achieved as individuals, recognising that the premise of oneness meant that the bliss of one became the bliss of all.

As she looked back at those months that had given birth to the Ether Group, life had seemed a whirlwind, a haze of activity. She had been so grateful that the boys' father, so devoted to his children and keen to nurture them in any way he could, had taken much of the responsibility for them when she had had to make so many trips during that time. The universe had, of course, put so many amazing synergies in place to ensure that disruption for the children was minimal, and she had, wherever possible, taken them with her, providing them with great adventures in their travels to so many places. After finally accepting all that was their contribution to each other, of those years they had been married, the love that had passed between them, Louise and her ex-husband had become firm friends.

The incredible emotion that welled up within her as she reflected upon the unprecedented number of awards won by the Ether Group, filled her once more with an overwhelming gratitude and knowing of how blessed she had truly been to be part of this incredible universal plan which had unfolded around her, around Ben and all those so close to her who had supported and loved her as the miracles had unfolded. So many had driven this foundation forward with such passion, such intent, in order to bring about all that was the universe's vision for oneness. She smiled to remember her deep sense of achievement when *The Sacred Quest* had swept the board at the Oscars, Grammies and Baftas. She had always known that this would be the case, for as she recalled, the moment that she originally conceived the book, she had been so adamant that she knew who would direct this film, and who would be cast in some of the key roles. What she had not realised then was that she would have such input into the film's direction and integrity, as it had been produced by Ether.

As she had arrived at the premiere, hand in hand with Ben, aghast at the crowds who merely wanted to speak to her yet were being held at some distance by the local police, she had kicked off her heels and leapt across the heads of the crowds (pretty adeptly as she remembered, for somebody who was already a few months with child), much to the dismay of the security, in order to talk to so many. As she had sat, cross-legged on a raised plinth above the crowd, a deep calm had descended as those around her listened to what she had had to say, and to what Ben had to say as He had calmly appeared behind her and, at her bequest, spoken in his incredibly enigmatic manner. These two, of course, delayed the screening of the film. However, under the circumstances, nobody seemed to mind.

This had been closely followed by one of her fondest memories. As Matt had stood on the stage of the Royal Opera House, hosting one of Ether's many charitable concerts, Louise had run onto the stage and sung with him. She had been closely followed by her children, whom Matt had promised to accommodate on stage in this manner. This had lead to an unprecedented influx of children from among the audience members surging forward and running to the stage, alight with inspiration to be the next famous musician. She, and the entire Opera House audience, had laughed with the wonderful feeling inspired by witnessing the delight upon these children's faces.

The Nobel Peace Prizes awarded to the Ether Group, reflected, to Louise, the very essence of the intrinsic changes they had made to the basis of life, to the right for the dignity of all, and for freedom of expression and truth for all. For the right for all to live a life truly abundant, as was their birthright. As predicted, a truly inspirational visionary had become involved with the group. His vision and drive to empower all through his incredibly successful microcredit schemes, had drawn he and Ether together. He was now so involved with the drive towards a Single World Federation, heavily committed to utterly transforming the intrinsic basis of life, of political vision and application upon the planet and, as Louise considered the energy of this man, she felt a surge of warmth flood her entire being.

As the work had forged ahead within the scientific centres, driving technology for harmonious inter-dimensional and universal travel forward, so had Adrian reappeared in Louise's life. Both she and Ben had embraced him as he had been so incredibly keen to work among them now, so very accepting and acknowledging of the love that passed between these two. As both a scholar within this lifetime and the recall of much ancient knowledge, he had brought to the fore astonishing knowledge to help pioneer some of the key areas that the Ether Group was working in. Louise considered how wonderful it had been that her boys had forged such a wonderful relationship so instantly with Ben, and laughed at their delight in welcoming into the family the notion of another sibling, as she and Ben had told them of the impending addition to their family. And as she grew, their daughter was beautiful, the image of her father, and, on the many occasions when Louise and Ben were apart within this physical reality, would address her mother in a manner which was entirely her father's.

As she heard the cue-call for one minute, Louise considered the very heavy trust that she and Ben had once more placed in the universe, as she had parted from Him some six months ago when He headed towards the southern hemisphere once more. Although they were never apart, always utterly one, and resuming the same relationship as that upon which they had rekindled their union all those years ago, she yearned in this moment for their physical touch to resume once more. She knew this had been part of their path from the outset, and she knew what lay ahead beyond this moment. Yet again she felt the overwhelming gratitude for the love of this her twin soul, and held within her heart, within her soul, all that was the union of their love across the ethers. It was with this knowing engulfing her being that she began to climb the stairs to the stage as the final cue rang out.

* * *

The world waited. Was she merely a writer gifted with extraordinary vision and imagination, or had she truly co-created with the universe a final step to raise the consciousness of humanity, to enable all of humanity to undeniably witness the elimination of all universal and galactic divides?

It was clear that she had been gifted with incredible divine guidance in achieving all of the changes instigated by the foundation. Yes, she had written a hugely successful novel, followed by a phenomenally successful film which had provided the ability to set up the Ether Group which was making incredible changes and moving the planet forward in consciousness and care. The world's population understood that the scientific, moral and ethical changes which had already taken place were almost beyond belief, as was her ability to have attracted and impassioned so many pioneers for the changes, those who were the very individuals that governments and people could no longer ignore. Surely this had to be the work of the universal source, the divine. But the world still wanted final proof, proof of this universal power in their own lives, proof that they were all the same, all part of one, proof that they could co-create their own existence with the universe. So many books, so many illustrations, so many guides were now available that detailed the manner in which all people could achieve just this, but none were as powerful as the living example witnessed with one's own eyes. And Louise was about to become just that example.

As she stood on the stage, in the middle of the stadium, all eyes gazing upon her, the world waiting eagerly for her every word, she felt no apprehension, no fear, only the deepest love for all of the beautiful universal beings who were with her now, supporting her as always, as ever. She thought of the many others who, like her and Ben, were located in prominent places around the globe at this precise moment and intently focused upon what lay ahead this evening. She called to Ben, all her energy reached out to Him, her very essence imploring Him to speak to her now, for although so many tens of thousands of miles separated them in this physical reality, they were, as ever, completely entwined, each one half of the other.

As Ben stood on the stage of the Opera House, so many eyes focussed upon Him, eager to hear what He would say, He heard her whisper, calling Him. He felt her energy caress his face, and He looked deep into the eyes of his beautiful treasure. With all his soul He desired to hold her in his arms, this beautiful woman he had found once more across time and space. His

thoughts in that moment took Him back to their parting those six months ago. She had been so insistent. 'We
are, and always will be, one' she had said. 'You came
back across all dimensions, all realities, all incarnations
to find me and love me, and I implored you to do so. As
surely as my love for you is bound to the magnificence
of the universe, so is yours for me. This incarnation is
but a blink in the moment of now, and we, my love, have
until creation's end to be together. We are twin souls, the
very first split of the same being. It matters not in physical form where we are, for now that we have both fully
returned to the light, our souls will always be joined.
It is because I love you with every essence of my being
that I know I am able to send you to fulfil the other half
of our soul's purpose. Can you not see that to be physically apart yet etherically together, is the only way that
we may achieve the final step to humanity's acceptance
and realisation of its spiritual destiny, its reality? People must finally have irrevocable evidence of their ability to exist in harmony, in unity, multidimensionally
and at soul level. Look how eager the world has been to
sweep aside the greatest love story of all time, of Jesus
and Mary Magdalene and their love of humanity above
their deep desire for physical life together, with all the
evidence there has been through the ages to support
this. This is the only way.' Tears coursed down his face
as He whispered his love for her and, in that very same
moment, she wept as she felt Him, heard his pain in
his whisper, experienced his pain at the memory of
their parting.

As the entire world watched, riveted to their television screens, to the huge screens erected above parks, deserts, forests, plains, in the valleys, upon the mountains, for all to experience, they were eager to know if this story really would end in the way that she had foretold within her book, if their own life story was to change irrevocably from now.

But Louise and Ben were oblivious to everything but their love for each other.

Both their auras were shining brightly now, both shrouded in a beautiful white-and-gold light. As the intensity of their love for each other, and for the entire universe, became so obvious to the world in those silent moments, a deeply moving and haunting music became audible. It was the very essence of the sea, of the air, of the mantra of souls calling each other, of all there ever was and ever could be to love. No orchestra or audio equipment or music of any kind had been planned. This music came from the universe and, as it grew gently louder, so the energy vibrations in the air grew astonishingly quickly. Not one soul on earth was oblivious to this shift. The light around them both started to change shape, growing in intensity, until, astonishingly, they were both standing before one another, she still physically in the arena in London, He still on the Opera House stage in Sydney. Oblivious to the gasps of the people within the arena, she reached up and held his beautiful face as He looked down upon her with that familiar, knowing smile she so adored. As she caressed his face, the people within the Opera

House were dumbstruck by her presence. He took her hands, held her hair and pulled her to Him, longing to feel her touch against Him. As they held each other so tightly, remembering that sacred ceremony so precious to them both eons ago in Atlantis, rekindled at The Wells, the words they whispered to each other could be heard clearly to all across time and space.

'We pledge our love to each other once more across the time-space continuum. Let the universe hold us always to this troth, always one being in two parts, always together.'

An incredible, blinding white light emanated from them and instantaneously flooded the stadium and the Opera House. It lit the skies around the world and in that moment it was as if the gateways of all dimensions had opened. The sky was alight, as if the universe had quite suddenly been restructured to accommodate every dimension the universal mind ever had, and ever could accommodate. These dimensions presented themselves in layer upon layer, as if unending circles of light being set out as creation's grid. Ethereal beings and holographic images were dancing in the dark of the night. Brightly-lit sacred geometric shapes, stunning crystalline structures, cosmic rays born of inter-dimensional origins were entirely visible to the naked eye. So many beings borne of the multi dimensions, parallel realities all gazed upon humanity. As the world tried to take in the enormity of what it was seeing and experiencing, these two and all who were positioned around the globe according to the planetary ascensions and within vortexes of energy became silent. In those moments of silence, the ascended masters appeared on the two stages simultaneously, bringing with them a knowledge that passed to all, that finally, we were to enter a new age of light, love and compassion. As the masters looked upon the joy and enlightenment on the faces of humanity around the world, they knew that the future was finally now, one to embrace.

The Hopi's prediction had been so accurate when they had said, 'We are the people we have been waiting for.'

And so it was.

Angels

by
Cherry Emery
www.emeryesoterics.co.uk

Angels in their natural state are beautiful balls of vibrant energy that manifest into the typical archetype of halo and wings just for mankind's convenience. There are trillions of angels; so many that they could never be counted.

Angels are extensions of the divine's love, having no free will of their own, and no karma. They are androgynous beings that move between dimensions at the speed of light, just by willing it. Angels are older than time, and were in existence long before humans; they tell us they will still be in existence when the last human has returned to source.

Angels are extremely powerful beings, and not at all the fluffy, fairy images portrayed on Christmas cards. Archangel Metatron's energy alone is said to be wider than that of the Earth. Angels who serve the Earth are subject to polarity, and divide into light and dark, not to be confused with good and evil. For every single thing on Earth there is an angel: every mountain, every building, even every flower.

Humans have their own angel and these are known as their guardian angels, a gift to each soul from the divine. The same guardian angel is present throughout every single lifetime that a soul incarnates, and carries a map of each lifetime within its presence. These guardian angels gently guide and steer us into the situations and emotions we have chosen to experience during that particular lifetime.

At any one time it is said that 100,000 incarnate angels live as humans upon the Earth. This they often find difficult, as they have never before experienced loneliness, and separation from the collective. They often display an innocence not generally seen in most people. They easily become stressed and depressed and so are in constant need of love and attention. Many suffer from dyslexia and often tinnitus. They make wonderfully loyal friends and can become gifted healers. Earth Angels have been known to manifest into what

Elemental Archangels

Archangel	Element	Region	Colour
URIEL	Earth	North	dark green/ brown
RAPHAEL	Air	East	pale blue/ white
MICHAEL	Fire	South	fire & electric blue
GABRIEL	Water	West	greens/blues
AZRAEL	Spirit	Centre	black

seems to be human form, in order to help humans during dire emergencies and then to disappear as quickly as they came.

In AD 560, the Dionysian hierarchy of Angels was established, and this is still very much accepted by the Churches today. Nine choirs of Angels were divided into three triads, the first triad, Seraphim, Cherubim and Thrones, never come to Earth, and are continually within the Divine presence. The second triad, Dominions, Virtues and Powers, are angels of the universe, and only help on Earth when asked to. The third triad, Principalities, Archangels and Angels, are the angels who are mainly involved with the Earth. Archangels are the most widely known, and are those to whom we can call for help.

Characteristics
In charge of ley lines, animals, vegetables & minerals. Call on for manifesting growth, wisdom & abundance.
In charge of healing and communication. Stands for vision and truth. Call on for help in both these matters.
Patron saint before St George. Call on for justice, protection and tie-cutting.
Dictated the Koran to Mohammed in AD 610. Told Mary she was to be Jesus' Mother. Call on for messages.
Archangel of death. Call on for alchemy, ceremony and magic.

Other well-known Archangels

Archangel	Colour	Characteristics
ZADKIEL	Violet	Works with St Germain and the angels of the Violet Flame. Call on for forgiveness, and transmutation.
JOPHIEL	Yellow	Call on to awaken your spirituality, for intuition and inspiration.
CHAMUEL	Pink	Call on for unconditional love and improving relationships.

Ascended Masters

by
Cherry Emery
www.emeryesoterics.co.uk

Each and every Ascended Master has lived between four and five thousand lives, living as a human being here upon the Earth. Through successive spiritual incarnations and emotional experiences they have transcended the spiritual laws of our reality, and ascended to a higher frequency than that of the Earth. They can remember all their past lives and live together as a collective of merged energy and light, as a group-mind, but they can also call upon the different aspects of the personalities of famous lives, for example Jesus for gentleness, St Germain for alchemy.

Their job is to help humans who call upon them for assistance and to guide us through the illusion of our existence, to light our path and help us all to recognise that part within our hearts that is divine. They also defend us from darker forces that would try to prevent us from evolving. Their motivation is unconditional love, but also on personal evolution, for if we do not move forwards and evolve spiritually, nor can they. So by helping us they help themselves.

There are tens of thousands of Ascended Masters, but only a few work with us here on the Earth. We only have to call their names and they will appear and help us, always asking that it be for the good of all and the harm of none.

I will list a few of the better known Ascended Masters together with what may be some of their past lives.

JESUS, conduit for the Christ Force known as Matreya Energy, known also in spirit as Sananda or White Feather. Past lives said to be Adam, Enoch, Joshua, Joseph, governor of Egypt, Krishna and Dionysus. Jesus' energy is loving and his touch gentle. He has an intense passion for mankind. Call on him to open your heart to find your own divinity, and to expand your consciousness. Also for truth, wisdom and physical grounding.

LADY NADA (soulmate to Jesus), most famous life as Mary Magdalene, thought to have also been Queen Nefertiti. In France she is depicted as the Black Madonna, the weeping queen searching for her lost love. She carried the feminine Matreya Energy known as the Shekinah Force. Call on her for joy, innocence, sensuality and sexuality, and to help with the inner child connection.

EL MORYA, thought to have been King Arthur, Ali Gobi, Melchior (one of the wise men) Thomas-à-Becket, and Thomas Moore. Known as the strictest master of discipline, call on him for leadership, strength and strategy in law and order.

LADY MIRIAM (soulmate to El Morya), most famous life thought to have been as Queen Guinevere, Lady of Lioness civilisation, aligned to earth healing and Earth's consciousness.

SAINT GERMAIN, also known as Count Ragoczy or the Wonderman of Europe. Works with the I AM affirmation, and custodian of the Violet Flame. Master of alchemy, ritual and ceremony. Teaches through challenge. Thought in previous lives to have been Merlin, Christopher Columbus and William Shakespeare.

LADY PORTIA (St Germain's soulmate), custodian of the Silver Violet Flame. Most famous life thought to be Morgan Le Fey. Her energy can seem to be quite dark and can be connected to the Void, but is always used for good, and transformation can be brought about through mystical feminine power.

LORD KUTHUMI, most famous past life St Francis of Assisi, also Pythagoras. Call on to help with sick animals or earth healing.

MOTHER MARY, gentle energy and Mother of Jesus. Call on to help with children. Ask her to step forwards and to heal your sick or troubled child.

KWAN YIN, worshipped as a goddess in China. Call on for compassion and for an answer to your prayers.

DJWAL KUHL, the Tibetan Master, wrote through Alice Bailey and Madam Blavatsky. Always seen smiling, with joyful energy. Call on to help, create calm from chaos.

The Ascended Masters are also known as 'The Brotherhood of Light', 'The White Brotherhood' and 'Brothers and Sisters of the Ascended Realm'.

Crystals

by
Cherry Emery
www.emeryesoterics.co.uk

Crystals are minerals which formed within, or on top of the Earth, hundreds of millions of years ago. The colour, shape and energy of the crystal will have been decided by the trace minerals that suffused the growing crystal at the time of its formation. Crystals are powerful because they naturally contain piezoelectric pulses, emitting pyroelectricity when heated, and kinetic electricity when struck. When the crystals are placed upon the body, these forces work with its bioelectrics to rebalance the human electromagnetic field and enhance the body's natural ability to heal itself.

Each and every crystal has its own healing properties, just as each and every person has their own unique energy and vibration.

As many crystals also contain a devic presence (a sort of angelic being), it is also important to honour and respect them, and to realise that they also play their part in the healing process. The moldavite heart pendant mentioned in this book is no ordinary crystal; it is a tektite, a meteoric gem from an exploded crystalline planet that fell to Earth 14.8 million years ago, in what is now the former Czechoslovakia. It is known for transformation, rapid spiritual evolvement, increased incidence of synchronicities, and is viewed as a relic of the legend of the Holy Grail.

Before using any crystals it is important to cleanse them. Run them under water for a few minutes (if the crystal's Mohs' Scale of hardness is high enough – at least number 3) or bury them in sea salt for a day. Don't forget, salt is a crystalline structure in its own right, so it will absorb negativity and must be disposed of after use. Dedicate crystals by assuring them you are using them for a positive purpose, and ask them three time to work for you, stating each time your intention. For example, when an apothalite is to be placed on your forehead, ask 'please absorb my headache', or if a citrine is to be placed on your solar plexus, ask 'please balance and heal my solar plexus chakra'.

Chakra Balancing with Crystals

Chakras are natural spinning vortexes of subtle energy. There are seven major chakras located on the human body, each with its own predominant colour. When these are out of balance, disease or health problems can arise on mental, physical or emotional levels around the particular area of the chakra that is unbalanced.

The seven major chakras and their related colours are located at the CROWN (white or mauve; amethyst or clear quartz), BROW (dark blue; sodalite or lapis lazuli), THROAT (light blue; larima or blue lace agate), HEART (green or pink; rose quartz, aventurine or bloodstone), SOLAR PLEXUS (yellow; citrine or yellow calcite), SACRAL (orange; carnelian or orange quartz) and BASE (red; red jasper or garnet).

In order to rebalance the chakras, lay down and place your chosen crystal upon each chakra centre. Allow the energy to be absorbed for around ten minutes.

Glossary of
Scientific
Explanations

Quantum Physics

Quantum physics is a branch of science that deals with discrete, indivisible units of energy called quanta, as described by quantum theory. There are five main ideas represented in quantum theory:

- Energy is not continuous, but comes in small, discrete units.
- Elementary particles behave both like particles *and* like waves.
- The movement of these particles is inherently random.
- It is *physically impossible* to know both the position *and* the momentum of a particle at the same time. The more precisely one is known, the less precise is the measurement of the other.
- The atomic world is *nothing* like the world in which we live.

While at a glance this may seem like just another strange theory, it contains many clues as to the fundamental nature of the universe, and is more important even than relativity in the grand scheme of things (if any one thing at this level could be said to be more important then anything else). Furthermore, it describes the nature of the universe as being very different from the world that we are able to see. As Niels Bohr said, 'Anyone who is not shocked by quantum theory has not understood it.'

Fractal cosmology

Cosmology has been based upon the assumption that when you look at the universe on the largest scale, matter is spread more or less evenly throughout space. This is named, by cosmologists, a smooth structure. Now, a group of researchers, led by statistical physicist Luciano Pietronero of the University of Rome and the Institute of Complex Systems, Italy, are pioneering a claim that galaxies form a structure that isn't smooth at all. Some parts of these galaxies have lots of matter, while others don't, but the matter always falls into the same patterns, in large and small versions, at whatever scale you look at. The universe is fractal, not linear or structured. A fractal universe undermines cosmology's basic assumption that matter is spread more or less evenly, something embodied in Einstein's cosmological principle.

Zero-point energy field

The zero-point energy field may be the most compelling news of our time. Not only is it likely to be providing 'free energy' in the relatively near future, but it is changing our whole cosmology, our worldview, our understanding and experience of existence. It is the true spiritual matrix of life. In the mid-twentieth century, quantum physicists first identified what seemed to lie at the heart of existence: an omnipresent energetic substructure (i.e. an energy interpenetrating everything) that moves 'Faster than Light' (FTL). As the century drew to a close, more and more experiments began demonstrating the validity of the theory. Science has, indeed, come full circle. Several hundred years ago, science, philosophy and religion were all the same body of study. They split apart in order to explore the nature of existence, each in its unique way, from a distinct orientation.

But science has now brought us back to looking at Source. This subatomic quantum field and zero-point energy have enabled scientists to recognise their potential use within space travel.

Dwarf Spheroidal Galaxies

The term 'dwarf spheroidal' is applied to the twelve low-luminosity dwarf elliptical galaxies that are companions to the Milky Way and to the similar systems that are companions to the Andromeda Galaxy. Although often thought in the past to merely be large, low-density globular clusters, detailed studies over the last twenty years or so have revealed that the dwarf spheroidal galaxies possess a more diverse set of properties and contain more complex stellar populations than the globular cluster analogy predicted. Since the individual stars in dwarf spheroidal galaxies can be resolved, their study will contribute to the understanding of the origin and evolution of dwarf galaxies in general.

An interesting result from more recent studies of the dwarf spheroidals is the indication that they, to a greater or lesser extent, show evidence for star formation over extended periods. This result was unexpected given that they have shown no sign of current or recent star formation and have almost no detectable hydrogen. They have a larger mass-to-light ratio than globular clusters, indicating that dark matter makes up large proportions of their masses.

Superstring Theory

Superstring theory is an attempt to explain all of the particles and fundamental forces of nature in one theory by modelling them as vibrations of tiny, supersymmetric strings. It is considered one of the most promising candidate theories of quantum gravity. Superstring theory is a shorthand for supersymmetric string theory because, unlike bosonic string theory, it is the version of string theory that incorporates both fermions and super-symmetry.

Neutrinos

Neutrinos are tiny, possibly massless, neutral elementary particles which interact with matter via the weak nuclear force. The *weakness* of the weak force gives neutrinos the property that matter is almost transparent to them. The sun and all other stars produce neutrinos copiously, due to nuclear fusion and decay processes within the core. Since they rarely interact, these neutrinos pass through the sun and the earth (and us) unhindered. Other sources of neutrinos include exploding stars (supernovae), relic neutrinos (from the birth of the universe) and nuclear power plants (in fact a lot of the fuel's energy is taken away by neutrinos). For example, the sun produces over two hundred trillion trillion trillion neutrinos every second, and a supernova blast can unleash 1,000 times more neutrinos than our sun will produce in its 10-billion-year lifetime. Billions of neutrinos stream through our bodies every second, yet only one or two of the higher energy neutrinos will scatter from us in our lifetimes.

The neutrino was proposed by Wolfgang Pauli in 1930, but it would be twenty-six years from then before the neutrino was actually detected. Pauli proposed the existence of the neutrino as a solution to a frustrating problem in a nuclear process called beta decay. It seemed that examination of the reaction products always indicated that some variable amount of energy was missing. Pauli concluded that the products must include a third particle, but one which didn't interact strongly enough for it to be detected. Enrico Fermi called this particle the neutrino, which meant 'little neutral one'. In 1956 Reines and Cowan found evidence of neutrino interactions by monitoring a volume of cadmium chloride with scintillating liquid near to a nuclear reactor.

Wolfgang Reines was jointly awarded the Nobel Prize in Physics in 1995, in part for this revolutionary work.

We know that the mass of the neutrino is approximately zero, but we are unsure how large the masses of the three individual neutrino types are, because of the difficulty in detecting neutrinos. This is important because neutrinos are by far the most numerous particles in the universe (other than photons of light) and so even a tiny mass for the neutrinos can enable them to have an effect on the evolution of the universe through their gravitational effects. There are other recent astrophysical measurements that provide information on the evolution of the universe and it is interesting to seek complementary information by direct determinations of the masses of neutrinos.

Particle Physics

Particle physics is a branch of physics that studies the elementary constituents of matter and radiation, and the interactions between them. It is also called 'high-energy physics', because many elementary particles do not occur under normal circumstances in nature, but can be created and detected during energetic collisions of other particles, as is done in particle accelerators.

We know about the three spatial dimensions of our everyday world, and Einstein added a fourth dimension, time. But there may be even more, possibly as many as eleven dimensions in the universe. This might explain why, of the four fundamental forces in the universe (strong, electromagnetic, weak, and gravity), gravity is actually so much weaker than the others – it could be leaking into an extra dimension! Again, particle physicists hope to find evidence of extra dimensions using powerful particle accelerators.

High-Energy Cosmic Rays

The history of cosmic ray research is a story of scientific adventure. For three quarters of a century, cosmic ray researchers have climbed mountains, ridden hot air balloons, and travelled to the far corners of the earth in the quest to understand these fast-moving particles from space. They have solved some scientific mysteries and revealed many more. The Pierre Auger Project continues the tradition as it begins the search for the unknown source of the highest-energy cosmic rays ever observed.

High-energy cosmic rays are a mystery.

Something out there – no one knows what – is hurling incredibly energetic particles around the universe. Do these particles come from some unknown superpowerful cosmic explosion? From a huge black hole sucking stars to their violent deaths? From colliding galaxies? From the collapse of massive invisible relics from the origin of the universe? We don't yet know the answers, but we do know that solving this mystery will take scientists another step forward in understanding the universe.

References

Aveila M, *I Remember Union*, New Britain, CT, All Worlds Publishing, 1992

Aviation Week and Space Technology, March 2004, William B Scott/Austin Texas article on advanced technology, 'To the Stars – zero-point energy emerges from realm of science fiction, may be key to deep space travel'

Brown, D, *The Da Vinci Code*, London, Bantam, 2003.

Byrne, R, *The Secret*, London, Simon and Schuster, 2006

Forsyth, K, Harvard ogham research, Buckuoy Proc soc antiq scot 125 (1995) 677-696

Hawkins, D, *Power vs. Force*, Carlsbad, CA, Hay House, 2002

Kenyon, T & Sion, J, *The Magdalen Manuscript*, Canada, Sounds True Inc, 2006

New Scientist Magazine, August 2007 'Through the keyhole – neutrinos seem poised to unlock the door to the Theory of Everything'

Plato, *Timaeus and Critias*, London, Penguin, 1974

Plato, *The Last Days of Socrates*, London, Penguin, 1962

Plotinus, *The Essential Plotinus*, New York, Mentor, 1964

Virtue, D, and Brown, L, *Angel Numbers*, CA, Hay House, 2005

Walsch, N D, *Conversations with God*, London, Hodder and Stoughton, 1999

Zukav, G, *The Seat of the Soul*, Surrey, Rider & Co., 1991

Plato's description of a discussion between Critias and Amynander, from Plato's Timaeus, pages 177 & 178 http://www.gutenberg.org/dirs/etext98/tmeus11.txt

Cherry Emery www.emeryesoterics.co.uk
Angel www.angelmajic.com
Edwin Courtenay www.edwincourtenay.co.uk
Diana Summer www.Dianasummer.com
Lynne McTaggart www.livingthefield.com

The Sacred Quest is also available to purchase as an audio CD at www.thesacredquest.co.uk, set entirely to an original soundtrack written specifically for the book by Matt Emery on behalf of The Ether Media Group.

The soundtrack is also available to purchase separately from the same website.